MORE®

My Ongoing Recovery Experience

The New You

Workbook 3

This workbook belongs to _____

Hazelden
Publishing

Hazelden Publishing
Center City, Minnesota 55012
hazelden.org/bookstore

ISBN: 978-1-61649-810-8

Editor's note

The names, details, and circumstances may have been changed to protect the privacy of those mentioned in this publication.

This publication is not intended as a substitute for the advice of health care professionals.

Readers should be aware that websites listed in this work may have changed or disappeared between when this work was written and when it is read.

The Twelve Steps are reprinted from *Alcoholics Anonymous,* 4th ed. (New York: Alcoholics Anonymous World Services, 2001), 59–60.

Alcoholics Anonymous, AA, and the Big Book are registered trademarks of Alcoholics Anonymous World Services, Inc.

The content in this workbook is from the Hazelden Betty Ford Foundation's My Ongoing Recovery Experience (MORE®) online aftercare program.

Cover design: Theresa Jaeger Gedig
Interior design: Terri Kinne
Developmental editor: Jodie Carter
Production editor: April Ebb
Copyeditor: Victoria Tirrel

Contents

Duplicating this page is illegal. Do not copy this material without written permission from the publisher.

iii

Overview of the MORE Program

MORE (My Ongoing Recovery Experience) is a program that offers education and guidance on essential recovery topics that will help you successfully manage the critical first year of your recovery. MORE can also be used for those just starting treatment or for those who have been in recovery for a while and want to renew or deepen their knowledge and skills.

Most addiction relapses—taking a drink or using after a period of abstinence—occur within the first eighteen months of recovery, with the majority happening in the first six months after an individual leaves treatment. It is important to identify your high-risk situations that pose a threat to your recovery and to make a plan for them, which will help you avoid relapse. Research suggests that if you can remain abstinent for at least one year after treatment, you have a good chance of staying sober—and maintaining your recovery for the rest of your life.

Overview of This Workbook: *The New You*

Workbook 3 is called *The New You* because it offers deeper guidance on putting recovery principles into action in your life and seeing that work pay off in significant personal growth.

What Key Topics Are Covered?

This workbook will help you learn how to recognize and avoid triggers, cravings, and "stinking thinking." You will continue to build spirituality and serenity, learn refusal skills, and learn how to say no to things that don't support your recovery. You will learn to use the ABCD (Action, Belief, Consequences, Dispute) technique to deal with challenging thoughts and emotions. This workbook will also help you improve your spiritual practice, learn about Steps Two and Three, and teach you how to break the cycle of anger and resentment. Other topics include deepening your connection with your Higher Power, dealing with fear and worry, and staying grounded as you continue to work the essential principles of recovery.

This workbook includes a variety of resources, such as:

- a Thought for the Day meditation or quote to accompany each topic
- education and skill-building on important early recovery topics
- activities that will help you practice self-reflection and put what you are learning into action
- "pocket power" Recovery Resources that you can keep with you for quick reference
- suggestions for Big Book readings on important topics
- websites for other recovery resources

As you complete the lessons in this workbook, you should start to see real growth and transformation in your life as you continue deeper work in recovery principles.

■ ■ ■

Know Your Triggers

Thought for the Day	*Success is not getting what you want; it's knowing what you don't need.*

INTRODUCTION TO TRIGGERS

You are especially susceptible to relapse in early recovery. Your stress levels are high as you go through intense emotional and physical changes. Research has shown that putting yourself in high-risk situations where you experience triggers and cravings can lead to a relapse. Triggers are people, places, objects, and feelings that cause you to have cravings to use alcohol or other drugs.

For example, if you would usually use when you were home alone in the evenings and feeling down, your triggers would be the following:

- being at home
- being alone
- evenings
- feeling neglected, lonely, or insecure

Your addicted brain associates these triggers with alcohol and other drug use. As a result of constant triggering and cravings, even one trigger can cause you to move toward alcohol and other drug use. This cycle of trigger/thought/craving/use can feel overwhelming.

Relapse Trigger Process

Trigger ▸ Thought ▸ Craving ▸ Use

STOP THE CRAVING PROCESS

An important part of recovery involves stopping this craving process. The first and easiest way to do this is to follow these three steps:

1. Identify your triggers.

2. Prevent exposure to these triggers whenever possible (for example, avoid being alone). Use the blank Daily Schedule form (found in the Recovery Resources section in the back of this workbook) to help plan your day to minimize exposure to triggers.

3. Instead of using, deal with these triggers in a different way (for example, calling someone when you are feeling neglected, lonely, or insecure).

Remember, triggers will affect your brain and cause cravings even though you are motivated to work your recovery program. Your intention to be sober must therefore translate into behavior changes that steer you clear of possible triggers.

KNOW YOUR UNIQUE TRIGGERS

It's essential that you know the people, places, things, emotions, and times of day that can trigger your brain to think about using alcohol and other drugs. You need to stay aware of the situations you feel are safe, low risk, high risk, or extremely dangerous for you.

The chart on the next page shows examples of common people, places, things, and emotions that are safe, low risk, high risk, and dangerous for some people in recovery. Your triggers will be unique to your experience.

Support your recovery by planning to do safe activities
with positive people who will be there for you rather than
trying any risky activities or situations.

ACTIVITY

TRIGGER CHART

Fill in the chart on the next page to create your unique list of people, places, things, and emotions that are safe, low risk, high risk, and dangerous for you.

Trigger Chart

SAFE	LOW RISK	HIGH RISK	DANGER
These are "safe" situations.	These are low-risk situations, but caution is needed.	These situations are high risk. Staying in these is extremely dangerous.	Involvement in these situations is deciding to stay addicted. Avoid totally.

Examples	*Examples*	*Examples*	*Examples*
• feeling grateful • being with friends in recovery • Twelve Step meetings • talking with your sponsor or counselor	• during work • watching TV at home • going out to dinner • driving to and from work or school	• holidays • celebrations where alcohol or other drugs could be present • during or after sex • feeling rejected • having too much free time	• spending too much time alone • feeling resentful • going to concerts or football games where you previously used alcohol or other drugs

If you feel the urge to use, go to a meeting,
or call your sponsor right away.

SAFE	LOW RISK	HIGH RISK	DANGER
These are "safe" situations.	These are low-risk situations, but caution is needed.	These situations are high risk. Staying in these is extremely dangerous.	Involvement in these situations is deciding to stay addicted. Avoid totally.

SUMMARY OF ACTIVITIES

This lesson focused on helping you identify and avoid your triggers. You identified the people, places, things, and emotions that are safe, low risk, high risk, and dangerous for you. Make sure you keep your daily schedule updated with a plan to avoid these triggers and replace them with safe, positive activities.

■ ■ ■

Duplicating this page is illegal. Do not copy this material without written permission from the publisher.

7

Deepen Your Understanding of Step Two

Thought for the Day	*Faith can move mountains. I pray that I may learn to depend less on myself and more on God.*

A HIGHER POWER

Before we worked Step Two, most of us didn't believe that we needed outside help to deal with our addiction to alcohol and other drugs. Before we focus on Step Two, let's quickly review key concepts from Step One.

Step One identifies the problem. In Step One, you admit you are powerless over alcohol or other drugs, and that your life has become unmanageable. It takes courage to take the first step.

Step Two introduces us to the solution.

Step Two:
"Came to believe that a Power greater than ourselves
could restore us to sanity."

As you work Step Two, you will see addiction as a spiritual problem that needs a spiritual solution. This means you need the help of others; you don't have all the answers. To live in recovery, you need to find a loving, guiding Higher Power you can really trust. A belief in God or religion isn't necessary. What is necessary is admitting that we can't achieve sobriety alone.

EMBRACING YOUR HIGHER POWER

When it comes to Step Two, many people struggle with the idea of a Higher Power and spirituality. What words or images come to mind when you imagine your Higher Power?

Remember, your Higher Power can be whatever you want it to be. You don't have to know who or what your Higher Power is right now—you just need to know that you aren't it.

To solve the problem of addiction, you need to surrender to accept help from others.

Sometimes it helps to think about the idea of a Higher Power this way:

- If you needed surgery, you would go to a surgeon.
- If you needed your taxes done, you would go to a tax accountant.
- So, if you have a spiritual problem, it's important to go to someone who knows more about the solution than you—and that someone is your Higher Power.

Your Higher Power could be God or your Alcoholics Anonymous (AA) or Narcotics Anonymous (NA) group. Most likely, AA and NA members know more about recovery than you. That's why it's important to "stick with the winners" and ask for help from the people whose sobriety you admire. It is always wise to seek help from others for things we don't know enough about.

Before we worked Step Two, the idea that a Higher Power is essential to our recovery may have seemed strange to some of us. You also may have questions or doubts about the role of religion in your recovery.

This is the reason Bill W. wrote chapter 4, "We Agnostics," in the Big Book. In it, Bill W. explains in detail how:

- A spiritual experience can happen to anyone.
- It isn't hard or unusual to believe in a Higher Power.
- You must believe in a Higher Power and have a spiritual experience to recover.

YOUR HIGHER POWER

Some of us hold beliefs from our past that make it hard to believe in a Higher Power. Explore this by answering the questions below.

1. Before you came to terms with your Higher Power, were there things in your past or things you believed that made you think it was going to be hard (or maybe even impossible) to believe in a Higher Power?

   _____

   _____

   _____

   _____

2. Did reading chapter 4, "We Agnostics," in the Big Book change your feelings about believing in a Higher Power?

   ☐ Yes   ☐ No

   If so, how?

   _____

   _____

   _____

   _____

3. How does the Big Book define a Higher Power? Use your own words to describe this.

   _____

   _____

   _____

   _____

HOW DO YOU KNOW IF YOU'VE GOT STEP TWO?

When you've worked Step Two, your thoughts, feelings, and behaviors will be more positive.

Check the things you find yourself thinking or doing.

☐ You need people.

☐ You don't have to have all the answers.

☐ You're learning a lot from your sponsor and other Twelve Step friends.

☐ There's nothing wrong with asking for help. It's not a sign of weakness. It's a sign of wisdom.

☐ There is a Power or Powers greater than yourself that can help you stay sober.

☐ You're feeling hopeful about the future.

☐ You can seek help for things you are struggling with.

If you checked many of the items above, then you understand what Step Two is all about.

WHY SPIRITUALITY IS IMPORTANT

We've been talking a lot about spirituality and the importance of focusing on spiritual things. Why? Because the strength of your spiritual foundation will help you through the changes you are facing in early recovery.

Spirituality makes a person whole. It gives meaning to life, and it is how you feel inside. It's also how you are connected with others, your Higher Power, yourself, and society as a whole. But what is this spiritual experience Step Two talks about?

To better understand the spiritual experience, read the Big Book, appendix II, "Spiritual Experience." Pay attention to what the Big Book says about having an open mind to spiritual ideas. It's impossible to recover from the disease of addiction if you close your mind to these spiritual ideas. Some people feel that a spiritual experience must be sudden and earth-shattering, but as we learn from the Big Book, a spiritual experience:

- is often a gradual process that happens over time
- is unique to each person
- needs to be experienced to understand it

Joe's Story

I had always been a partier who used with a lot of friends. But still there was always this nagging loneliness inside of me. The problem was that getting high was at the center of all our time together.

I couldn't figure out if my friends really liked me, or if they just liked the fact that I would get high with them. After being in the program for a while, I decided to make my Twelve Step group my Higher Power. Then I decided to take a risk and began to tell this group who I really was, without the drugs. It was scary at first. What if they didn't like who I was? But slowly I began to feel an acceptance that I'd never experienced before. I realized these new friends were there for me, and they really knew and liked me. It made me feel really good inside.

Like Joe, once you begin to trust in a Power greater than yourself, you will begin to see gradual changes in yourself and begin to feel different inside. This is what a spiritual experience is.

SPIRITUAL PROGRESS

Below are signs of spiritual progress along with the opposites of spiritual progress. Check any of these signs of progress that you see in yourself:

☐ surrendering to a Power greater than yourself—rather than playing God

☐ being someone who is humble—rather than someone who is humiliated

☐ being spiritually fit—rather than having a spiritual sickness

☐ being open to positive lessons—rather than focusing on trials and tribulations

☐ being open to learning new things—rather than being a victim

☐ being part of a healthy fellowship—rather than being apart or separate from others

☐ inspiring others—rather than being someone who aspires to be something different

☐ learning from mistakes—rather than repeating mistakes

☐ being someone who responds—rather than someone who reacts

☐ being happy, joyous, and free—rather than restless, irritable, and discontent

continued

If you've noticed any of these positive changes in your attitudes, behavior, or thinking, then you have had a spiritual experience, and you are growing in spiritual ways.

WHAT STEP TWO MEANS BY INSANITY

The last part of Step Two talks about the need to be restored to sanity. So you may be thinking to yourself, "Does this mean my drinking and using other drugs made me insane?" That may be a little hard to believe, so let's complete the Picturing Insanity activity.

ACTIVITY

PICTURING INSANITY

This activity will help you take a closer look at this concept of insanity and get a clearer picture of what is meant in Step Two about the need to be restored to sanity.

Step Two:
"Came to believe that a Power greater than ourselves
could restore us to sanity."

The Big Book includes many examples of people who thought they could control their alcohol use but were wrong. The lie that people with addiction tell themselves is, "I'll be able to drink and use other drugs like other people." Believing and acting on this lie is what is meant by insanity. Once we realize that we are not able to control our use of alcohol or other drugs, we are acting with more sanity.

One explanation of insanity is "doing the same thing over and over again but expecting different results."

Check the boxes to indicate your answers to the questions below.

1. Do you still think you can safely use alcohol or other drugs like your nonaddicted friends, even though the results are always the same—that your use causes problems in your life?

   ☐ Yes   ☐ No

2. If you said "yes" above, can you see how this thinking is part of the insanity described in Step Two?

☐ Yes   ☐ No

Before you started recovery, when you wanted to test your willpower, maybe you thought, "I can have just one drink or hit." But most likely, that one drink or hit turned into many because your obsession to drink and use other drugs caused you to ignore the truth and believe the lie—that you can drink alcohol and use other drugs like other people.

Step Two happens when you realize that you
are not able to control your use of alcohol or other drugs.
You will always need to work the program
and practice complete abstinence.

HOW RECOVERY RESTORES US TO SANITY

"Sanity" is defined as realizing that without a spiritual change or partnership, there will be no change in your using. You have to make this change in order to get better results. Sanity is also building a life based on spiritual principles and the truth—that sobriety is the only answer.

Are there ways that you have experienced a taste of sanity in recovery? Have you felt more gratitude, serenity, and peace? Do you feel more honest and hopeful? Sanity is more than just abstaining from use. It's also about finding new ways to live, think, and relate to others.

How do I know if I've worked Step One?
I am no longer baffled by my disease.

How do I know if I've worked Step Two?
I feel a glimmer of hope that change is possible.

SUMMARY OF ACTIVITIES

This lesson taught you how to deepen your understanding of Step Two. This includes embracing your Higher Power, knowing why spirituality is important, and understanding what is meant by "restore us to sanity" in Step Two. Make sure you read chapter 4 in the Big Book, "We Agnostics," and appendix II in the Big Book, "Spiritual Experience." These will help you understand why spirituality is such an important part of recovery.

■ ■ ■

Awaken Your Spirituality

Thought for the Day	*"I pray that I may be calm and let nothing upset me. I pray that I may not let material things control me and choke out spiritual things."* —*TWENTY-FOUR HOURS A DAY*, JANUARY 21

SPIRITUAL GROWTH

As we progress in early recovery, we focus on practical things like abstaining from drinking and using other drugs, and identifying high-risk situations. *But the foundation of all change in recovery is spiritual.*

We need to grow spiritually, because it will impact how we feel about ourselves and others. In Step Two, we learned about believing in a Power greater than ourselves. This is spiritual. But spirituality also means improving how we think and act each day.

WHAT IS SPIRITUALITY?

The concept of spirituality is a very personal one. Spirituality is the quality of our relationships with ourselves, our Higher Power, those closest to us, and our community at large. It includes our values, our priorities, the way we interact with others, and our concept of a Higher Power.

When we were drinking and using other drugs, we often "played God." We acted as if we believed that we had ultimate control over our lives. We thought we were "right" and that others needed to change to our way of seeing things. We searched for happiness but found a spiritual void inside. We tried to fill that void with drugs, but we may also have tried to fill that void with material things, such as clothes or jewelry. Some of us tried to fill the spiritual void with unhealthy behaviors, such as binge eating or compulsive technology use, and that still didn't fill the void. If we remain this spiritually bankrupt, we will relapse back to using alcohol and other drugs.

WE NEED A SPIRITUAL AWAKENING

A spiritual awakening can be described as a change in attitude, behavior, and thinking. This does not need to be a huge event. It is often a gradual process that comes naturally from working a recovery program.

As we work the program, our self-centeredness, anger, resentments, and shame begin to leave us. We are more understanding and helpful to others. We are beginning to like ourselves.

Check any of these signs of spiritual awakening that you notice in yourself.

- ☐ feeling greater peace and serenity
- ☐ feeling more connected to other people
- ☐ finding life has meaning without using alcohol or other drugs
- ☐ finding that you need less and less control over life and others
- ☐ finding yourself more accepting of others
- ☐ enjoying the simple things in life, like enjoying nature

Ramon's Story

By the time I got to treatment, I was mad at the world. I took my anger out on my family. I was convinced they didn't understand my problems. If only my circumstances were different, I would have been just fine. This was insanity! I have been sober for five years now.

Looking back, I can see that I was what they call a "dry drunk" for the first two years. I did some things right—I went to meetings regularly, read the Big Book, and didn't pick up the first drink. But I didn't work the Steps with a sponsor, and I carried around this anger and resentment.

It finally came to me in a Twelve Step meeting when we were talking about resentments. This was my spiritual awakening. I realized that I had been carrying around anger toward my wife and family for making me go to treatment. Suddenly a huge weight was lifted, and my whole attitude changed. My family noticed almost immediately! I was lighter when I replaced resentment with gratitude toward my family for being there when I needed them the most.

ACTIVITY

YOUR SPIRITUAL AWAKENING

Answering the questions below will help you see opportunities to improve.

In what ways are you not fully working the Twelve Step program?

_____

_____

_____

How might you be holding back on fully accepting your sponsor's advice?

_____

_____

_____

Do you secretly believe that someday you can go back to using?

_____

_____

_____

How do you think you are different from others when it comes to facing the disease of addiction?

_____

_____

_____

How can you start to improve your program of recovery this week?

_____

_____

_____

■

Duplicating this page is illegal. Do not copy this material without written permission from the publisher.

19

IMPROVE YOUR SPIRITUALITY

There are four ways you can start to improve your spirituality.

1. Start a Spiritual Practice

For most people, life is frequently fast-paced and stressful. We need time to sit back and gain perspective on what we are here for and how we behave in our daily lives. This reflection and introspection—looking inside oneself—can be done through prayer and meditation. Meditation and prayer are spiritual tools. They can help you let go of your own willfulness, bring a sense of calm and well-being, deepen your relationship with your Higher Power, and help you discover your Higher Power's will.

2. Learn about Prayer

In the past, you may have prayed frequently or never have prayed. If you don't believe in prayer, try acting as if you do and see what happens. We call this "Fake it 'til you make it," which means that as you begin to act with spiritual principles, you will begin to grow spiritually. Whether or not you believe in the power of prayer does not matter right now. The important thing is to begin prayer and meditation with an open mind. You have nothing to lose and everything else to gain.

3. Try the Serenity Prayer

Your prayers do not have to be complex. The Serenity Prayer may be as much as you can do:

> God, grant me the serenity
> to accept the things I cannot change,
> courage to change the things I can,
> and wisdom to know the difference.

4. Learn about Meditation

Meditation is listening to your Higher Power. You can use meditation to clear your mind of racing thoughts, center yourself, and let go of fears, jealousy, blame, and control. When you meditate, you learn to listen to your inner self. When your mind is racing with too many stressful thoughts, focus on your breathing: slow down and take full, long breaths. With practice, you'll be able to use deep breathing to clear your mind for several minutes and eventually even longer.

MEDITATION PRACTICE TIPS

1. **Prepare the environment.** Pick a specific place and time for your meditation practice. Find a safe place that is free from distractions. Shut the door and unplug the phone.

2. **Enter a state of relaxed alertness.** Many spiritual traditions, such as yoga, emphasize posture. Try sitting upright with a straight spine. This promotes attention and relaxation at the same time. Find a posture that feels good and that allows you to breathe deeply.

3. **Allow for uninterrupted silence.** Being silent frees you from the compulsion to speak, criticize, or justify yourself. In this silence, you can listen and gain direction for your life.

4. **Listen and give acknowledgment.** Listening is the state of being tuned in and open to the guidance of your Higher Power. When you receive guidance, stay open and thankful.

Check some of these spiritual things to practice this week:

☐ prayer—talking to your Higher Power

☐ meditation—listening to your Higher Power

☐ taking time every day to enjoy the wonders of nature

☐ connecting with other people each day

☐ noticing and embracing positive spiritual changes in yourself

SUMMARY OF ACTIVITIES

This lesson taught you how to deepen your spirituality and what is meant by spiritual awakening in the Twelve Steps. Try starting a new routine by adding a morning or evening meditation or prayer as a daily spiritual practice.

■ ■ ■

Improve Your Support System

Thought for the Day	*"[Courage is] a quality of mind which enables us to deal with the problems and realities of life without reliance on alcohol."*
	—*THE LITTLE RED BOOK*

ACTIVITY

TYPES OF SUPPORT

You've been hearing this a lot: "Support from others is essential to your recovery." Before you started working the Twelve Step program, your social network likely included people you got drunk or high with, or those who enabled you to continue drinking and using other drugs. Rather than holding on to our old friends and habits, how about starting to shape a support network that can really support, help, and inspire you?

Social support comes in many forms, but it can be easily broken down into distinct kinds: emotional, practical, informational, and reflective. Let's see how your support breaks down.

Emotional Support

Emotional support comes from people who support you emotionally and reach out to you in times of need. They ask you how you're doing, acknowledge your feelings, and let you know they love you. Emotional support can come in a phone call, a hug, or someone just sitting with you quietly.

Who are the people you can count on for emotional support?

_____

_____

continued

Duplicating this page is illegal. Do not copy this material without written permission from the publisher.

23

Informational Support

Informational support is advice, suggestions, and information that people give you. If a friend tells you about a job opening or gives you advice on how to fix your car, that's informational support. When people at an Alcoholics Anonymous (AA) or Narcotics Anonymous (NA) meeting tell you where to go for clean-and-sober fun, that's informational support.

Who are the people you can count on for informational support?

_____

_____

Reflective Support

Reflective support helps you see yourself and situations more clearly. People may support you by sharing their experience to offer you a different perspective. They may offer advice on something they know a lot about. You can learn from others' experience and apply it to your life.

Who are the people you can count on for reflective support?

_____

_____

Practical Support

Practical support is tangible aid or service. An example is someone giving you a ride to meetings or the grocery store when your driver's license is suspended. You might need help with a school assignment or with child care for your children. Or someone may generously offer to cook a meal for you.

Who are the people you can count on for practical support?

_____

_____

EVALUATE YOUR SUPPORT SYSTEM

Is your current support system helpful or harmful? There may still be people in your support network who have the potential to influence you negatively. Place your efforts on bringing helpful, positive, healthy relationships into your network. Build your core of emotional support (which may include your spouse or friends in recovery), as well as your secondary support (people who help out in other ways, such as your case manager).

Not only do you want to be able to turn to your support system when you are having a problem, but you also want to think about building a healthy network for the long haul—one that can also help you reach your goals. Supporters not only help you in the bad times, they can help you in the good times, too.

ACTIVITY

IMPROVE YOUR SUPPORT SYSTEM

Now let's take a closer look at the people you currently spend time with.

1. Who are the people you spend time with who make you more likely to drink or use other drugs?

   _____

   _____

2. Can you take a "vacation" from any of these people for a while? How would you do that? Are there people in your life with whom you don't use alcohol or other drugs?

   _____

   _____

3. Would you be able to rely on your clean-and-sober friends for support (if you don't already)? How might you approach them to ask for help?

   _____

   _____

   _____

continued

4. Do you ever feel more like using if you have just had a fight with someone? When was the last time this happened? Whom can you talk with for support the next time you get angry or frustrated?

_____

_____

5. Do you ever feel more like using when you are lonely? When was the last time this happened? Whom can you talk with for support the next time you feel lonely?

_____

_____

_____

As you spend more time in recovery, your support system will change. You will need to evaluate your support system frequently in early recovery.

As a living, changing thing, your support system will give back to you as much as you put into it. So remember to thank your supporters when they help you. And let them know you'd be glad to return the favor in their time of need.

Remember to keep the Recovery Wallet Card with you for easy reference so you know whom to call for help and where to attend a Twelve Step meeting nearby. (A blank copy of the card is found in the Recovery Resources section at the end of this workbook.)

SUMMARY OF ACTIVITIES

This lesson taught you how to keep improving your support system of utilizing a sponsor, healthy friends, family, and people in Twelve Step meetings. You learned about the difference between emotional support, informational support, reflective support, and practical support. Keep utilizing people in all of these areas so that you are fully supported in your recovery.

Avoid Stinking Thinking

Thought for the Day	*"The world doesn't need super men or women, but super-natural people. People who will turn the self out of their lives and let Divine Power work through them. Let inspiration take the place of aspiration. Seek to grow spiritually, rather than to acquire fame and riches. Our chief ambition should be to be used by [our Higher Power]. The Divine Force is sufficient for all the spiritual work in the world."*

—*TWENTY-FOUR HOURS A DAY,* FEBRUARY 15

ACTIVITY

STINKING THINKING

"Stinking thinking," also known as addictive thinking, describes the irrational thoughts that keep us stuck in addictive behavior. Addictive thinking involves negative attitudes, distorted thinking, and an intense resistance to change. While you were using alcohol or other drugs, you probably invented all sorts of ways to justify using while trying to avoid negative consequences.

Below are examples of stinking thinking. Getting rid of stinking thinking is essential because these irrational thoughts leave you vulnerable to a relapse.

Check any of these statements of stinking thinking (or irrational thoughts) that sound familiar to you:

☐ "I can control my drinking and/or drugging. One drink or hit won't make me lose it."

☐ "I'm not going to drink or use again, even if I hang out with my friends who do."

continued

- ☐ "It's not hard to get along in a Twelve Step group. Just tell people what they want to hear."

- ☐ "I'm sure I could go back to using socially without a problem."

- ☐ "Changing isn't that hard."

- ☐ "Poor me. My life is so hard right now that I deserve a drink."

- ☐ "I only use drugs because other people make my life so hard. I'm not the problem; other people are the problem."

- ☐ "If it can't be perfect, then it's not worth doing."

What are some examples of stinking thinking from your past?

_____

_____

_____

_____

_____

_____

_____

_____

REPLACE IRRATIONAL THOUGHTS WITH ACCURATE THOUGHTS

Think of some accurate thoughts or beliefs that can replace your irrational ones. For example, below is an irrational thought replaced with a more accurate thought. Say both of these thoughts aloud. Does the accurate thought feel more rational when you say it aloud?

Irrational: "I can control my drug use. One drink or hit won't make me lose it."

Accurate: "I have the disease of addiction. I can't use any amount of alcohol or other drugs like people who do not have addiction. I must remain completely abstinent and not use any drugs, ever. This is necessary to protect the healthy life I've started in recovery."

OTHER EXAMPLES OF ADDICTIVE THINKING

Below are other examples of addictive thinking and the attitudes that go along with it, as well as ways to remedy them.

Lip Service

An example of lip service is saying, "I promise I'll never do it again," when you know that you will do it again.

Have you ever made promises that you knew you couldn't keep? Lip service is when you say things you don't really mean to get someone's approval. You might say, "I'll never stay out all night again," or "I will never use drugs again." We may believe these statements when we make them, but we don't follow through. Talk is cheap, but actions speak louder than words. Recovery means examining our attitudes and honoring our commitments. Part of our spiritual work is to regain our trust in ourselves and build others' trust in us. We start by taking our commitments seriously and following through with what we say. We no longer use our words to get away with things.

The remedy to lip service is to speak the truth and follow through with what you say. Can you take situations where you've used lip service in the past and imagine yourself telling the truth instead? What would you say to be more truthful?

_____

_____

_____

_____

_____

Grandiosity

An example of grandiosity is thinking, "I am strong enough to quit after just one drink."

Grandiosity describes feelings of being superior or more capable than you really are. For example, you believe that you can stay sober on your own. You think you have total control over your alcohol or other drug use. You tend to overinflate your abilities. You require perfection in everything. You find it hard to admit mistakes. You find it hard to let others help you because they don't do things as

Duplicating this page is illegal. Do not copy this material without written permission from the publisher.

29

well as you do. You may believe that you are different from others with addiction—you are smarter, stronger, or better than others. The truth is that it doesn't matter how smart you are. People functioning at the highest intellectual levels are just as vulnerable to addiction as anyone else.

Some people use grandiosity as a way to cover their vulnerability. For example, they may feel worthless but still think they are better than other people with addiction. If you have had grandiose thoughts, you are not alone. Many people struggle with this type of stinking thinking.

The opposite of grandiosity is honesty, humility, and truth. We can practice these virtues by knowing that we don't have all the answers. We can take responsibility by saying, "I'm sorry; I got that wrong," or "I don't know the answer to this problem. I could use some help." Grandiose thoughts don't mix with spirituality. You can't grow spiritually while you still believe that you have all the power and all the answers. What grandiose thoughts have you had? Can you think of ways you can be more honest and humble?

_____

_____

_____

_____

_____

_____

Rationalization

An example of rationalization is thinking, "I don't need to go to a Twelve Step meeting today. I am feeling great, and I have more important things to do."

Rationalization is when you give reasons that sound good but aren't really true. We use rationalizing thoughts to justify or make excuses so that we can get our way. Rationalizing will make you cut corners in your recovery, such as not going to meetings or not really working the Twelve Steps. Rationalizing can lead you to deny the reality of your addiction. All of these things make you more vulnerable to a relapse.

Do you notice yourself rationalizing as a way to avoid doing things you need to do for your recovery? Think about the last time you had some thoughts of rationalization. What would be a more honest way to present the facts that does not justify or excuse your behavior?

_____

_____

_____

_____

_____

_____

_____

Injustice

An example of injustice is thinking, "Why me? Why is my life so hard?"

Some people tend to be hypersensitive and feel that the world is unfair to them when things don't go their way. It's easy to blame others for making our life hard. This kind of stinking thinking creates resentments and can be hard to let go of. Part of life is dealing with adversity. Everyone has problems, no matter who they are or where they are in life. You might get really frustrated when a cashier gets your order wrong or someone cuts you off when driving.

Handle thoughts of injustice by changing your expectations. None of us have the right to expect that everything will go right all the time. All of us have to deal with frustrations. Nothing in life is perfect. Once we realize and accept this, we feel better. When we adjust our expectations to be more realistic, we can shift our emotions toward the positive, and this frees us up to feel better. What thoughts of injustice have you had?

_____

_____

_____

_____

_____

_____

_____

ACTIVITY

IDENTIFY YOUR PATTERNS

Check any of the following that describe some ways you engage in irrational or stinking thinking.

- ☐ **lip service:** when you say things you don't really mean to get someone's approval

- ☐ **grandiosity:** feelings of being superior or more capable than you really are

- ☐ **rationalization:** you give reasons that sound good but aren't really true, and you use those to justify or make excuses so that you can get your way

- ☐ **injustice:** you are hypersensitive and feel that the world is unfair when things don't go your way

To remedy these patterns of thinking, you can be more truthful and quickly admit your mistakes. You can also accept that we all deal with frustrations in life—you aren't entitled to have things go perfectly all the time. What can you do to improve your thinking?

_____

_____

_____

_____

_____

_____

_____

_____

_____

_____

_____

STOP ADDICTIVE THINKING FROM LEADING TO A RELAPSE

Cravings don't always happen in a straightforward, easily recognized way. A thought about using alcohol or other drugs may pass through your head with little or no effect. But a thought about using that you continue to think about will cause cravings and is the beginning of a relapse. The further you allow the thoughts to go, the more likely you are to return to using.

Relapse Trigger Process

To help you stop addictive thinking, think about the important reasons why you are working hard on recovery. The next activity will help you think about the people you care about and your goals. Even if you completed this activity before, it can be helpful to revisit it and see if your reasons for recovery have changed over time.

ACTIVITY

REASONS TO STAY SOBER

Think about the reasons why you want to stay sober and live a life in recovery—how being in recovery has positively impacted your life. Keep your reasons personal and specific. Make sure your reasons are about gaining something positive for yourself and not about avoiding something negative. Provide as much detail as you would like.

Reason 1

_____

_____

_____

Reason 2

_____

_____

_____

continued

Reason 3

_____

_____

_____

■

PRACTICE THOUGHT-STOPPING TECHNIQUES

If you find yourself unable to stop thinking about using, you can use thought-stopping techniques to quiet these thoughts. It is very important to stop the thought as soon as possible to prevent it from building into an overpowering craving that makes you vulnerable to a relapse.

Try these five thought-stopping techniques, and use those that work best for you.

1. **Visualization.** Picture a switch or a lever in your mind. Imagine yourself actually moving it from "on" to "off" to stop the addictive thoughts. Have another picture ready to think about in place of those thoughts.

2. **Snapping.** Wear a rubber band loosely on your wrist. Each time you become aware of addictive thoughts, snap the band and say no to the thoughts as you make yourself think about another subject. Have a subject ready that is meaningful and interesting to you.

3. **Relaxation.** Feelings of hollowness, heaviness, and cramping in the stomach are cravings. You can often relieve these feelings by filling your lungs with air and breathing out slowly. Do this three times. You should be able to feel the tightness leaving your body. Repeat this whenever the feeling returns.

4. **Call someone.** Talking to another person provides an outlet for your feelings and allows you to hear your own thinking process. Keep with you at all times phone numbers of people who are supportive of your recovery.

5. **Prayer and meditation.** Taking time to center ourselves and focus on our Higher Power will help in resisting cravings.

The first step in changing stinking thinking is to recognize it. With practice, you will get better at refuting irrational thoughts, and you will be able to stop recurring thoughts of using from turning into cravings and potentially leading to a relapse.

SUMMARY OF ACTIVITIES

This lesson taught you how to recognize and avoid stinking thinking and how to replace irrational thoughts with more accurate thoughts. Make sure you also keep your Recovery Wallet Card with you at all times so you know whom to call for support and the name and address of a Twelve Step meeting you can attend. The End Your Lapse tips on the Recovery Wallet Card will help you if you do relapse.

■ ■ ■

Duplicating this page is illegal. Do not copy this material without written permission from the publisher.

35

Build Serenity

WHAT IS SERENITY?

Serenity is peaceful balance, despite life's challenges. It suggests a calm and quiet state of well-being. Serene people live in the here and now, instead of dwelling on the unhappiness of yesterday or the fears of the future.

MAKING ROOM FOR SERENITY

What gets in the way of serenity? As people with the disease of addiction, what we often seek is a sense of absolute control. We are seeking something that is simply not possible for human beings. This quest for control can ruin our peace and serenity.

The desire for control has two aspects:

1. **We try to control the behavior of others.** We may cling to this strategy despite its repeated failure. We can't control what others think, say, or do.

2. **We try to control our feelings by medicating them with alcohol or other drugs.** This strategy is also doomed to failure because eventually we build up a tolerance to alcohol or other drugs, and then they no longer work as well to mute our feelings. Then we get stuck in the addiction cycle of needing more of a drug in hopes that it will make us feel better. Using drugs to medicate our feelings leaves us with more problems and feeling even more hopeless than when we started.

Duplicating this page is illegal. Do not copy this material without written permission from the publisher.

37

WHY DO WE SEEK CONTROL?

For some of us, our need for control may be a response to the unmanageability caused by our out-of-control use of alcohol or other drugs. For others, we may seek control as a means to get our way or to avoid suffering. Our quest to control things that we can't possibly control only leads to misery that drives us to use alcohol and other drugs. Either way, finding serenity will help you loosen your grip and find peace in the present circumstances, whatever they are.

1. Identify one specific example where you have tried to "control" the behavior of others, situations, or events.

    _____

    _____

    _____

    _____

2. What impact did that behavior have on you and your recovery process?

    _____

    _____

    _____

    _____

3. What are some healthier behaviors that you can practice that can produce better outcomes?

    _____

    _____

    _____

    _____

WHAT CAN YOU GAIN FROM ACCEPTANCE?

Acceptance helps us with serenity because it teaches us to come to terms with "what is." Acceptance is an important part of your recovery. When you learn acceptance, you'll let go of judgments that block you from an honest view of yourself and others.

Part of our work in early recovery is in acknowledging our disease and accepting that we can never use alcohol or other drugs again. This can seem like a loss of freedom at first. But what we gain is freedom of body and spirit. Once you start to manage the disease of addiction, your body will heal, and you will feel better. You will grow spiritually and become more at ease with yourself and others. Things that used to upset you will no longer bother you. Your relationships with others will improve. When you make this realization, you understand that trading the use of alcohol or other drugs for health, happiness, and serenity is a great bargain.

As you practice acceptance and serenity, what would you like to gain? For example, better relationships with parents, friends, or children? Or a better job or better health?

_____

_____

_____

_____

PRACTICE THE SERENITY PRAYER

In early recovery, the Serenity Prayer can take on a very simple meaning: we cannot change the fact that we have the disease of addiction. We must pray for the ability to accept this. What we can change is how we respond to this diagnosis. We can choose to continue to drink and use, or we can courageously choose the road of complete abstinence. This means we accept that we can never use any amount of alcohol or other drugs. Not ever. We also accept that things in life will happen—both negative and positive—that are outside our control. We can't control everything in life, but we are responsible for the effort we make.

"God, grant me the serenity
to accept the things I cannot change,
courage to change the things I can,
and wisdom to know the difference."

—Serenity Prayer

ACTIVITY

LETTING GO OF CONTROL

1. Do you try to control people or situations in ways that cause you a lot of tension and agitation? Describe below.

   _____

   _____

2. Do you believe that you could avoid pain or loss if you could only exert your will over your job, over family members, or over other people? Describe below.

   _____

   _____

   _____

3. Do you blame yourself for things that go wrong even though they are outside your control? For example, a broken-down car, a job layoff, a debilitating illness, or hail damage to your car? Describe below.

   _____

   _____

   _____

Try to surrender some of these to the wisdom of your Higher Power. Remember that serenity is the opposite of control. We can have one or the other, but not both.

BUILD SERENITY WITH MEDITATION

Meditation is all about listening to your Higher Power. The object of meditation is to clear your mind of racing thoughts, center yourself, and let go of fears, ambitions, jealousy, blame, and control. When you meditate, you will learn to listen to your inner self.

Whenever your mind is racing with too many stressful thoughts about what you should be doing, what needs to be done, and what you should have done two weeks ago, focus on your breathing, and make a conscious attempt to slow down and take full, long breaths. Soon you'll be able to use deep breathing to clear your mind for several minutes and eventually even longer. When obsessive, stressful thoughts catch up with you, simply refocus your breathing. Keep practicing this, regardless of how many times it takes before you see concrete results.

BUILD SERENITY WITH PRAYER

Another way to build serenity is to set aside time every day for prayer. In the past you may have prayed, "God, get me out of this, and I promise I'll never use drugs again." Prayers like this are self-serving. Instead, pray for the courage to change and to confront things that threaten you or make you angry. Pray for others, even those you don't like. Use prayer to relieve the worry and anger that could cause you to relapse back to alcohol or other drug use.

Below is an example of a prayer that you can use daily. When you wake up, think about the twenty-four hours ahead. Consider your plans for the day. Before you begin, ask God or your Higher Power to direct your thinking. If you don't believe in God, you can say this prayer to your Higher Power:

> I pray that I may choose the right way.
>
> I pray that I may live to give to others and learn the secret of abundant living.
>
> I pray that I may be very grateful today.
>
> I pray that I may feel that God's love will never fail.
>
> I trust that God's will guides me today.

BUILD SERENITY WITH FELLOWSHIP

Another way to build serenity is by spending time in fellowship with people in Twelve Step groups, such as Alcoholics Anonymous (AA) or Narcotics Anonymous (NA). Listening to others will help you feel less alone in your struggles. Talking about your fears, pain, and resentments will help you release their burden.

USE THE DAILY SERENITY PLAN

As you explore your spirituality, you can start building your serenity by doing just one small action each day. Try this seven-day plan as a way to add serenity to each day of the week.

Day 1: Don't judge anyone today, not even yourself.

Day 2: Do something nice for someone, but don't tell anyone about it.

Day 3: Give everyone you see—including strangers—a big smile.

Day 4: Practice gratitude. Spend a few minutes in a quiet place and think about how fortunate you are to have what you have, no matter how simple.

Day 5: Say the Serenity Prayer as often as you can.

Day 6: Say a prayer of compassion for someone you don't like. This helps to cleanse anger and resentment out of your heart.

Day 7: Share your story at a Twelve Step meeting in order to help yourself and others.

SUMMARY OF ACTIVITIES

This lesson taught you how to build serenity and spirituality. It included guidance on improving your spirituality and serenity by letting go of controlling behaviors, practicing acceptance, and practicing meditation and prayer. Try to incorporate more spiritual practices into your days in the next week.

■ ■ ■

Handle Emotions Using the ABCD Technique

Thought for the Day	*"Alcoholics are not saints . . . ; we will still feel and experience anger. The important thing is to check yourself from venting anger unjustly upon someone else, or from holding on to anger and letting it turn into a resentment, or from turning it inward upon yourself so you feel unworthy and depressed."*
	—*THE LITTLE RED BOOK*

ACTIVITY

IDENTIFY YOUR FEELINGS

We all have emotions, such as joy or grief, that we can learn from. Emotions are neither good nor bad; they just are. The issue isn't what emotions we should have, but what the best way is to handle them. Think about the last week. What emotions did you experience? Were there times when you felt patient, grateful, or joyful? Were there times when you felt sad, mad, or discouraged?

Identifying your emotions is an important skill to practice every day.

Look over the feelings list and check off the words that describe how you are feeling right now. You can have more than one feeling at a time, so check off all the feelings that apply.

"The past has no power over the present moment."

—Eckhart Tolle

continued

Feelings List

- ☐ amused
- ☐ angry
- ☐ annoyed
- ☐ betrayed
- ☐ caring
- ☐ competent
- ☐ complete
- ☐ confident
- ☐ delighted
- ☐ dependent
- ☐ despairing
- ☐ discounted
- ☐ discouraged
- ☐ disgusted
- ☐ distant
- ☐ eager
- ☐ encouraged
- ☐ envious
- ☐ excited
- ☐ fearful
- ☐ frightened
- ☐ fulfilled
- ☐ giving

- ☐ glad
- ☐ grateful
- ☐ grief stricken
- ☐ guilty
- ☐ happy
- ☐ hesitant
- ☐ hopeful
- ☐ hostile
- ☐ hurt
- ☐ immobilized
- ☐ impatient
- ☐ inadequate
- ☐ irritated
- ☐ isolated
- ☐ jealous
- ☐ joyful
- ☐ lonely
- ☐ loving
- ☐ mad
- ☐ optimistic
- ☐ overwhelmed
- ☐ patient

- ☐ pessimistic
- ☐ pitiful
- ☐ proud
- ☐ rageful
- ☐ regretful
- ☐ resentful
- ☐ revengeful
- ☐ sad
- ☐ scared
- ☐ shameful
- ☐ strong
- ☐ sympathetic
- ☐ tender
- ☐ trusting
- ☐ untrusting
- ☐ unwanted
- ☐ useless
- ☐ vulnerable
- ☐ wanted
- ☐ warm
- ☐ wary
- ☐ weak

You can use this activity to record your emotions each day so that you become better at identifying how you feel. Remember, there is no such thing as a "bad" emotion. Emotions just are. It is how we react to them that matters. If you are struggling with challenging emotions, talk with your sponsor, your counselor, or a supportive friend.

HOW FEELINGS CAN LEAD TO RELAPSE

All of us experience challenging or painful emotions, such as regret, grief, and many others. Our first reaction may be to try to reduce the pain we feel, but we often do this in destructive ways. For example, have you ever isolated yourself, hurt yourself, started drinking, or used drugs when you were feeling regret, shame, grief, or anger?

In the past, we may have tried to control these challenging emotions by medicating them with alcohol or other drugs. This strategy may have worked for a while, but it eventually fails because we need more and more of the drug to feel better. Using drugs as a way to deal with our feelings leaves us with more problems than when we started.

We must find a healthy way to deal with feelings
so we don't see using as the answer.

CHANGE YOUR THINKING

Maybe you've heard the saying "Change your thinking, change your life." You may not realize it, but your thoughts and feelings are closely connected. What you think about a situation affects how you will feel about it. The reverse is also true. What you feel about a situation affects what you think about it. In addition, your actions can influence how you feel and think. For example, if you are feeling discouraged about recovery, you can take action. Go to a meeting, call a friend in recovery, or spend time meditating and connecting with your Higher Power. By taking positive action you will feel more positive about your situation. This is known in Alcoholics Anonymous (AA) as "Fake it 'til you make it." The more you think and act positively, the better you will feel.

Duplicating this page is illegal. Do not copy this material without written permission from the publisher.

45

APPLY THE ABCDs TO IMPROVE HOW YOU FEEL

The ABCD technique is a model that can help us think and act more rationally. The first part of this technique is best seen as a math equation: **A + B = C**

The **action** (or triggering event) + your **belief** (what you tell yourself about the event) = **consequences** (your resulting feelings and actions).

You can't change what happened (the consequences), but you can change what you *believe* about the situation. We do this by examining our beliefs about what happened. Often, we have inaccurate or self-defeating beliefs that cause us to feel negative emotions about the situation. We can identify our inaccurate beliefs by **disputing** our logic (the D in ABCD) and embracing more accurate beliefs about the situation.

You can use the ABCD technique to deal with any feeling, such as anger, shame, worry, grief, and more. With practice, you will be able to use the ABCD technique to slow down your reactions to challenging situations and evaluate your beliefs to make sure they are accurate before you react.

ACTIVITY

REDUCING SHAME

In this activity, you will use the ABCD technique to deal with feelings of shame.

Many people with addiction carry shame over their past use of alcohol and other drugs. We blame ourselves for harms done to family members. We will use this example of shame below:

A—Describe an ACTION or event that you feel ashamed about.

I am ashamed about _____.

Example: I am addicted to alcohol or other drugs.

B—Describe your BELIEFS and thoughts about the action.

I am ashamed because I believe _____

_____.

Example: I should be able to control my drinking and drug use. I am a bad person.

C—Describe how you felt and what you did about the action (the CONSEQUENCES).

I feel _____.

This causes me to _____.

Examples: I feel ashamed. I am not good enough to be around people. This causes me to avoid my friends and family.

D—The next step is to DISPUTE your logic.

Is there any evidence that your beliefs about this situation are true?

_____

Is there a more helpful, accurate way of looking at the situation?

_____

_____

Here are two examples of more accurate beliefs about addiction and how it affects you:

1. Addiction is a disease. It cannot be controlled by my willpower; therefore, I have a bad disease, but I am NOT a bad person.

2. I am a good person who is working hard to recover from the disease of addiction. As I manage this disease, I will work to repair my relationships with friends and family.

When you can embrace these two accurate beliefs about addiction, you'll find it easier to let go of any shaming beliefs you had about addiction.

Today, practice positive steps to honor your recovery.

Duplicating this page is illegal. Do not copy this material without written permission from the publisher.

47

TAKE POSITIVE ACTION

Another thing we can do to change how we feel is to take positive action. If you are struggling with feelings of shame and blaming yourself for the hurts you caused others when you were drinking or using, you can go to an AA or Narcotics Anonymous (NA) meeting. Talking with others in recovery will help. Knowing that you are doing the work needed to manage the disease of addiction will not magically get rid of all of your pain, but it will help you feel better. With each right action you take to support your recovery, you will feel better until one day, you will be surprised at how good you feel about yourself.

SUMMARY OF ACTIVITIES

This lesson taught you positive ways to handle challenging emotions before they lead to a relapse. This includes instruction on the ABCD technique to dispute inaccurate beliefs. Use the Identify Your Feelings activity to record the emotions you feel each day so that you become better at identifying how you feel. Go to an AA or NA meeting and talk about any challenging emotions you are feeling. Ask your sponsor or friend in recovery to help you dispute any faulty beliefs that are causing you pain.

■ ■ ■

Practice Refusal Skills

Thought for the Day	*"When you seek to follow the way of the spirit, it frequently means a complete reversal of the way of the world that you had previously followed. But it is a reversal that leads to happiness and peace. Do the aims and ambitions that a person usually strives for bring peace? Do the world's awards bring heart-rest and happiness? Or do they turn to ashes in the mouth?"* *—TWENTY-FOUR HOURS A DAY, JANUARY 28*

KNOW WHEN TO SAY NO

One of the most important skills you can learn in avoiding high-risk situations is the skill of saying no to things that could harm your recovery. We are often afraid to say no because we think people won't like us or that we will hurt someone's feelings. Even if we do say no, it may be hard for us to say no a second time if it didn't work the first time.

Learning how to say no in a firm, respectful way is an essential life skill. When you are faced with a risky situation, a simple and direct no is often the best solution. If you want to (or feel you have to) give an explanation, you should keep it simple: "No, I can't go with you," or "No, I don't go to bars." You might say, "No, sorry. I am afraid I have to decline." Don't over-explain or defend your decision. Be graceful and honest. You might say something like, "I'm sorry, but it's just not possible for me to do that," or "I have to decline, but thank you anyway."

Think about these three situations:

1. You've been sober for two months when your friend offers you a drink. You tell your friend no, but he says, "C'mon. I'm not asking you to get drunk. Just one quick drink, and we'll go on our way."

2. A friend wants you to go to the movies, but it would mean that you would miss the Narcotics Anonymous (NA) meeting you normally attend. You are stressed and could really use the meeting, but you don't want to hurt your friend's feelings by not going to the movie.

3. Your neighbor frequently asks you to watch her son "for just a minute, while I run to the store." This errand usually turns out to be a couple of hours. You want to say no but don't want to offend your neighbor.

Keep your daily schedule updated with healthy activities. (You can find a blank Daily Schedule form in the Recovery Resources section at the end of this workbook.) This will make it easier for you to say no when someone asks you to do something risky that you should decline.

PRACTICE SAYING NO

When you start practicing refusal skills by saying no, you may get some pushback, especially if people are not used to hearing no from you. People may try to get you to change your mind and say yes. If you feel pressured, stay calm, make eye contact, and continue to say no. If the person doesn't listen after two or three times, leave the situation.

Try saying:

- "I can't do this right now."
- "No, thanks. Not this time. Thank you for asking."
- "Sorry, but no."
- "Please accept that I cannot come."

Be assertive:

- Start the sentence with the word "no."
- Shake your head and use nonverbal assertiveness to emphasize your no.
- Use a clear and direct voice.
- Keep eye contact.

Other Tips

- Avoid passive communication. We are often passive when we don't feel confident saying no. We may look down, avoiding eye contact. Our tone of voice may be quiet. We may say no in a way that is not clear.

- Avoid aggressive communication. Aggressive communication happens when we yell or blame others. We may use a harsh or sarcastic tone that is disrespectful of others.

SAY NO TO HIGH-RISK SITUATIONS

Below are three examples of high-risk situations that require you to say no in order to protect your recovery. Practice the way you would say no to each of these risky situations:

1. Some of the guys from work ask you to join them for happy hour on a Friday evening. You can protect your recovery by saying:

   _____

2. You are at a wedding where someone insists you toast the bride and groom. You can protect your recovery by saying:

   _____

3. You run into your old drug dealer unexpectedly, and he wants you to go for a drive. You can protect your recovery by saying:

   _____

4. If you didn't say no to these situations, what negative consequences would result?

   _____

   _____

   _____

5. Do you agree that learning to say no in these situations will greatly reduce your risk of relapse?

   ☐ Yes   ☐ No

SUMMARY OF ACTIVITIES

This lesson taught you how to practice positive refusal skills and how to say no to things that could harm your recovery. Make sure you keep your daily schedule updated with healthy activities, which will make it easier to say no to the things you need to avoid to protect your recovery.

■ ■ ■

Change Your Thinking

Thought for the Day	*"In A.A. [or other Twelve Step programs], we forget about the future. We know from experience that as time goes on, the future takes care of itself. Everything works out well, as long as we stay sober. All we need to think about is today. When we get up in the morning and see the sun shining in the window, we thank God that He has given us another day to enjoy because we're sober, a day in which we may have a chance to help somebody."*
	—*TWENTY-FOUR HOURS A DAY,* MARCH 21

SELF-DEFEATING BELIEFS

Stinking thinking and irrational beliefs can compromise your recovery. The following are some ways to overcome stinking thinking and common irrational beliefs.

Self-Defeating Belief 1: "I should never be uncomfortable—physically or emotionally. Life should be pain free."

This self-defeating belief has to do with not wanting to deal with pain and discomfort. When you expect your life to be free from suffering, you are holding on to a self-defeating belief that holds you back in your spiritual growth and raises your risk of relapse.

Wouldn't a life free of pain be delightful? Certainly. Is it realistic? No. Your life is not going to become pain free even if you are working hard on your recovery.

Can you relate to this self-defeating belief? Think about the last time you felt emotional or physical pain. Check the items on the next page that reflect how you felt and what you did.

Duplicating this page is illegal. Do not copy this material without written permission from the publisher.

53

Did you:

- ☐ tell yourself that you shouldn't have to feel pain and suffering

- ☐ feel resentful or blame others for the painful situation

- ☐ use alcohol or other drugs to try to reduce the pain

In the past, many of us sought a quick escape from our pain. Our first instinct was to reach for a drink or hit. That instinct to avoid pain is in all of us, so it is important to accept that we all sometimes experience pain and suffering. Life is full of uncomfortable situations.

If we don't accept this truth, we will constantly feel resentful, blame others for our problems, and think we are being treated unfairly. When we accept that some suffering is part of life, we begin to accept life on life's terms, and we are able to preserve our peace and serenity, which will help our recovery.

As you work on practicing acceptance, you will obtain a greater peace and serenity. This will make life seem easier, but it will only come with time.

Self-Defeating Belief 2: "I must never be inconvenienced. I should always have things my way!"

This self-defeating belief has to do with not wanting to deal with inconvenience and annoyance. When you expect your life to be free from inconvenience and annoyances, you are holding on to a self-defeating belief that holds you back in your spiritual growth and raises your risk of relapse.

Many of us do not accept the reality that life is sometimes bothersome and inconvenient. We can't always get what we want when we want it. We get stuck in traffic. Our dentist is running thirty minutes late. Our car breaks down on the highway. The annoyances in life can cause us to become impatient, unforgiving, angry, and resentful. It is hard to find serenity when we feel so annoyed.

Can you relate to this self-defeating belief? Think about the last time you felt annoyed or inconvenienced. Check the items below that reflect how you felt and what you did. Did you:

- ☐ tell yourself that you shouldn't have to be annoyed or inconvenienced

- ☐ feel resentful or blame others for the annoying situation

- ☐ use alcohol or other drugs to try to deal with feeling so bothered and annoyed

Self-Defeating Belief 3: "Life should be fair!"

This self-defeating belief has to do with not wanting to deal with unfairness in life. There is a saying that expecting life to be fair is like expecting a lion not to eat you just because you didn't eat him. Life isn't something we possess and control; rather, it's something we take part in and witness.

There are many things in life that aren't fair. For example, in early recovery, we are making an effort to change, but others may not yet believe our new commitment to abstinence and recovery because we've broken promises in the past. Instead of thinking how unfair these people are being, remember that they are giving you a second chance. You have to regain the trust of those you may have let down in the past.

Bob's Story

In recovery, I feel like a new person, but some of my friends and coworkers seem skeptical to believe my recovery is real. I mentioned to my sponsor that it didn't seem fair, and he reminded me that it will take time for others to adapt to the "new me." I had been stuck in all-or-nothing ways of thinking: my friends and family were either with me or against me. In reality, they want me to be healthy and productive. As long as I stay clean and sober, my family will start to see my recovery is real.

Can you relate to this self-defeating belief? Describe in the space below.

_____

_____

_____

_____

_____

_____

As we practice more acceptance knowing that sometimes life isn't fair, this helps us stay grounded and maintain our serenity.

Self-Defeating Belief 4: "I know best. I should be in control."

This self-defeating belief has to do with wanting to get our way and thinking that we know best. When you were actively drinking and using other drugs, you may have thought you had everything under control, but in reality your life was out of control. Now that you've been sober for a while, don't let yourself think you have control over your substance use. It's easy to fall back into this kind of thinking.

Eugene's Story

In early recovery, I had a lot of trouble working Step One, admitting that I was powerless over alcohol and other drugs. I'm a strong-willed person, and I wanted to recover, but I wanted to control my addiction with sheer willpower. It was hard for me to let go. After going to meetings, I realized that others felt the same way. Over time, I've learned there's a certain relief and freedom in letting go of controlling everything and trying to be perfect. I feel more relaxed, serene, and comfortable with myself.

"While we may not be able to control all that happens to us, we can control what happens inside us."

—Benjamin Franklin

Like Eugene realized, admitting that you can't control everything is key. Otherwise, this faulty thinking could lead you back to active drinking and drug use. What you do have control over is the daily act of humbly admitting your powerlessness over alcohol and other drugs.

Can you relate to this self-defeating belief? Describe in the space below.

_____

_____

_____

_____

_____

Self-Defeating Belief 5: "I should never have to ask for help.
If I ask for help, I'll look stupid or weak."

This self-defeating belief has to do with wanting to be capable in every situation and to avoid any sign of weakness. When we first started in recovery, many of us were not comfortable asking for help, but we learn that reaching out to our support system is essential. With your support system's help, you can accomplish something that you cannot do by yourself—sobriety. You just have to ask. This means making the effort to turn to others for guidance and help.

Jake's Story

Nine weeks after treatment, I went to a work party, and they had an open bar. Being there gave me strong urges to drink, but my sponsor and I had made a plan to deal with triggers. I looked in my wallet and took out the list of people I could call for help. I called my sponsor. He talked to me while I left the party. That phone call saved me from a relapse.

Like Jake, the more you reach out for help, the easier recovery will become.

Can you relate to this self-defeating belief? Describe in the space below.

_____

_____

_____

_____

_____

_____

_____

We all need help sometimes. Have you ever heard the saying, it's not the heavy load that breaks us, but the way that we try to carry it? Asking for help is a sign of strength, not weakness.

Duplicating this page is illegal. Do not copy this material without written permission from the publisher.

57

Self-Defeating Belief 6: "Rules are for others; I'm different."

This self-defeating belief has to do with wanting to get our way, regardless of how it affects others. We may think that we know best and that the rules don't apply to us. Being rebellious can get you in trouble with other people because you're looking out for your own good instead of thinking of others' needs. This type of attitude can also stop your progress in recovery.

José's Story

Before I got into treatment for heroin addiction, I always rebelled against authority. I was proud to say that I made my own rules to live by. I routinely drove as fast as I wanted and came to work as late as I wanted. In early recovery, that rebellious attitude blocked me from admitting that I was powerless over substance use and blocked me from turning my will over to my Higher Power. Talking to others in recovery helped me realize that I wasn't better, smarter, or more entitled. I needed to surrender to a lifestyle of love, gratitude, and humility. When I did, I began a never-ending spiritual journey. I no longer battled against my life. I learned to love my life instead.

Can you relate to this self-defeating belief? Describe in the space below.

_____

_____

_____

_____

_____

_____

_____

_____

Self-Defeating Belief 7: "Other people, places, and things govern how I feel."
This self-defeating belief has to do with not wanting to take responsibility for how we feel. By blaming others for how we feel, we avoid having to change ourselves and to face our own mistakes. Nothing is ever our fault. This keeps us stuck in the past. The truth is that we have the power to make positive decisions and to act in positive ways.

Charlotte's Story

When I found a sponsor, I talked to her about my tendency to be a perfectionist and to get frustrated, angry, and anxious when things didn't go my way. Working the Steps and practicing acceptance have helped reduce my stress and improve my relationships; they've helped me understand that it is okay for me and for others to make mistakes. Mistakes are an opportunity to learn and improve. We are all works in progress.

Can you relate to this self-defeating belief? Describe in the space below.

_____

_____

_____

_____

_____

_____

_____

_____

"Our very first problem is to accept our present circumstances as they are, ourselves as we are, and the people about us as they are. This is to adopt a realistic humility without which no genuine advance can even begin."

—Bill W.

Self-Defeating Belief 8: "I focus on external things to feel good."

This self-defeating belief has to do with relying on external things for happiness. When we focus on things outside ourselves, like material possessions, people's opinions, or our personal status, we rely on these things to bring us happiness. This is what we did when we used alcohol and other drugs. We relied on drugs to make us happy.

Mary's Story

Before treatment, I used drugs because they made me feel more confident, fun, and relaxed with my friends. When I was around people, I often felt anxious and inadequate. Now that I've been sober for nine months, I can see that I was using drugs to make me feel better about myself. Working the Steps has set me on spiritually solid ground. Now when I feel fearful, anxious, or lonely, I meditate and pray to my Higher Power. I also have great sober friends who understand my problems and accept me for who I am.

Can you relate to this self-defeating belief? Describe in the space below.

_____

_____

_____

_____

_____

_____

_____

_____

_____

_____

OVERCOME SELF-DEFEATING BELIEFS

How can you stop all of these self-defeating beliefs from tripping up your recovery? Start performing a daily inventory where you evaluate how your day went and look at the kinds of self-defeating beliefs that crept in.

ACTIVITY

ABCDs OF SELF-DEFEATING BELIEFS

Once you've identified your self-defeating beliefs, try changing them with the ABCD technique.

A. Action: Describe an action or event where you felt a self-defeating belief creep in. Example: Your friend disagreed with you.

_____

_____

_____

_____

B. Beliefs: What beliefs or thoughts did you have? Example: "He should not have disagreed with me! I'm always right!"

_____

_____

_____

_____

C. Consequences: Describe how you felt and what you did. Example: "I was so upset with my friend that I yelled at him, slammed the door, and drove directly to the bar for a drink."

_____

_____

_____

_____

D. Dispute: Dispute your thinking and beliefs by asking yourself, "Who said so? What is the evidence? Is there a more helpful way to look at this situation?" Example: "Why must I always be right? Is it possible that my friend had a valid point? Even if I were right, did I really need to yell?"

_____

_____

_____

_____

SUMMARY OF ACTIVITIES

This lesson taught you the importance of addressing stinking thinking and irrational beliefs, including how to overcome eight common self-defeating beliefs. Anytime you encounter self-defeating beliefs, you can use the ABCDs of Self-Defeating Beliefs activity to challenge and adjust your thinking.

Break the Anger Cycle

Thought for the Day	*"If we give out hate, we will become hateful. If we are resentful, we will be resented. If we do not like people, we will not be liked by people."*
	—*TWENTY-FOUR HOURS A DAY,* NOVEMBER 7

THE ANGER CYCLE

Anger is not a positive or a negative emotion—it just is. What makes it positive or negative is how we handle it. Expressing our anger inappropriately creates problems. We fall into a cycle of responses that keeps us stuck. When we think we are treated unfairly or feel we lack control, we may become angry. If we don't identify and resolve our anger, it can grow into resentment.

Anger leads to resentment, which leads to more negative feelings, which lead to more anger and possibly a relapse back to substance use. To avoid a relapse, learn to handle your emotions so you can stop this negative cycle. Stopping the anger cycle will lift a burden off your shoulders.

The Anger Cycle

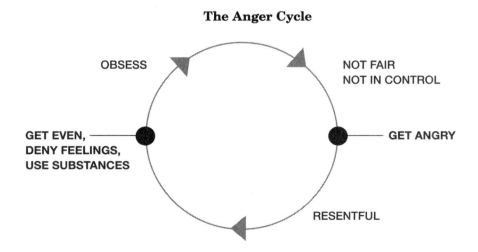

Duplicating this page is illegal. Do not copy this material without written permission from the publisher.

63

As our resentments build, we may try to handle them by doing the following:

- **Denying that we feel resentful.** We keep stuffing our resentments until we reach a breaking point or we direct the anger inward on ourselves.

- **Trying to get even.** We may take an outwardly aggressive stance or quietly seek revenge in a roundabout way. Either method hurts our relationships with others.

- **Using alcohol or other drugs to temporarily relieve the discomfort.**

As you can imagine, none of these are healthy solutions. If our anger is not resolved, it grows, and the cycle repeats itself.

UNDERSTANDING ANGER

We all have feelings of anger. Anger is a natural and normal response to situations where we feel threatened, violated, or cheated. There are lots of legitimate reasons to be angry. If someone mistreats you or hurts you, or if you witness an injustice, it's natural to feel angry. These are common sources of anger. It's important to remember that even when we feel justified in our anger, we still need to manage our response so that we don't inflict more pain on ourselves or those around us. It can help to talk with your sponsor or counselor about any situations that cause you to feel angry.

When anger remains unresolved, it can lead to feeling resentful. Resentment is the opposite of forgiveness, and it keeps us stuck at the point where we were hurt. By holding on to these hurt feelings, we continue to suffer.

It's important to learn how to manage our feelings appropriately. Why? Unresolved anger and resentments can be triggers to drinking and using other drugs. The good news is that you can learn to break this cycle of anger.

ACTIVITY

IDENTIFYING SOURCES OF ANGER

Many of us experience anger that holds us back in our spiritual growth.

Check any of these sources of anger in your life.

- ☐ **Control.** When you find yourself having urges to control or manipulate others, you are bound to feel unhappy when things don't turn out your way. When we feel angry about not having control, the world seems as though it's out to get us. One way we can let go of control is to practice the Serenity Prayer: "God, grant me the *serenity* to accept the things I cannot change, courage to change the things I can, and wisdom to know the difference." There are always a few things we can let go of for now. Letting go can help us reduce our stress and save our energy.

☐ **Defensiveness.** Anger can be used, consciously or unconsciously, as a way to keep people at a distance or as a way to get them to give in to our wishes. Can you think of times when you used anger in this way? Using anger as a defense enables us to keep people from getting close to us.

☐ **Masking pain.** Anger can also be used to mask other feelings, such as grief, hurt, loss, or fear. When you hide these types of feelings, people cannot understand what is really bothering you. Remember, they cannot give you the help and support you need when you don't let them in. Think of a time when you tried to mask your real feelings by getting angry. This anger, if not managed in healthy ways, may turn inward.

ACTIVITY

MANAGE ANGER

You can use the ABCD technique to manage anger by examining your beliefs as sources of anger. The technique is described below:

A. Describe an **ACTION** or event that left you feeling angry.

B. What **BELIEFS** or thoughts did you have about this action or event?

C. Describe how you felt and what you did in reaction to this action or event (the **CONSEQUENCES**).

D. **DISPUTE** your thinking by asking yourself, "Who said so? What is the evidence? Is there a more helpful way to look at this situation?"

Answer the questions below using an example from your life.

A. Action: Describe an action or event that left you feeling angry.

_____

_____

continued

_____

_____

B. Beliefs: What beliefs or thoughts did you have about this action or event?

_____

_____

_____

_____

C. Consequences: Describe how you felt and what you did in reaction to this action or event.

_____

_____

_____

_____

D. Dispute: Dispute your thinking and beliefs by asking yourself, "Who said so? What is the evidence? Is there a more helpful way to look at this situation?"

_____

_____

_____

_____

Using the ABCD technique can help us press "pause" on our knee-jerk anger reaction, so we can shift our thinking toward a more rational and balanced reaction. For example, instead of getting angry at another driver for pulling in front of you on the road, pause and tell yourself, "It's unfortunate that other people sometimes drive poorly, but it's a fact of life. Many people do try to obey the rules and drive safely. Having that driver almost hit me was scary, but in the end, I'm okay and my car didn't get wrecked and I didn't get hurt." Using this type of self-talk can help you reduce your anger and start to regain your calm.

LET GO OF RESENTMENTS

Resentment comes from unresolved anger. It grows out of a belief that you have been wronged. Maybe you're still holding on to an old insult, or you're mad that you made compromises for someone who caused you pain or misfortune. You may feel cheated because someone else got something you wanted, such as love, attention, or financial or social success. Maybe your relationship with someone caused you to lose something important to you.

Many of us may still hold on to resentments from long ago, and if we don't address these resentments, they leave us vulnerable to a relapse.

Are you holding on to any resentments from things that happened in the past? What do you resent? How does holding on to this resentment make you feel? Describe in the space below.

_____

_____

_____

_____

Holding on to resentments only leaves you feeling bitter. Resentment will eventually crowd out your other feelings, such as joy, compassion, and happiness, leaving you without serenity and peace. Feeling miserable like this long enough can make you feel righteous and justified in seeking revenge. This may mean getting drunk just to get back at someone who hurt you. But this philosophy doesn't work. It's like punching yourself in the stomach to get back at someone else.

In the past, we used alcohol or other drugs to deal with challenging feelings such as anger, fear, disappointment, and grief, and now we need to understand and manage these feelings before they cause us to start thinking about alcohol or other drugs as a quick fix to escape these emotions.

Read "Freedom from Bondage" in the Big Book in the section Personal Stories, part III. This story suggests that one way to let go of a resentment against another person is to pray for the person and wish for his or her health and happiness. Even if we don't really mean it at first, as we practice this prayer over time, we find that

continued

Duplicating this page is illegal. Do not copy this material without written permission from the publisher.

67

eventually we let go of our bitterness toward the person and feel more compassion and love. After you read the Big Book, ask yourself if you are holding on to any resentments. Are you willing to work to let these go?

If you are having trouble letting go of resentment, talk with your sponsor, counselor, or Twelve Step friends. Ask for ideas on how to resolve the situation. To reduce your stress, go for a run or walk, or pound a pillow. Get your emotions out by writing a letter about them that you never intend to send—and then let those emotions go. Sometimes resolving the situation is out of your control. When you have done all that you can do, just let the situation go and accept it. The worst thing we can do is obsess about something we can't change.

PRACTICE POSITIVE CONFLICT RESOLUTION

In early recovery, it's really important to avoid stress and conflict, but some conflicts in life just can't be avoided. Follow these steps to practice positive ways to handle conflict.

1. **Cool off before reacting.** Stay calm and don't raise your voice or assume a threatening posture. If you are having trouble staying calm, imagine yourself pressing a "pause" button in your brain to stop the knee-jerk angry reaction. Or try counting to ten before responding. If you can't calm down, it's best to leave the situation until you can calmly discuss the issue. Use the ABCD technique to help you slow down and question any inaccurate logic and beliefs that may be fueling your anger.

2. **Use "I-Messages."** If, after using the ABCD technique, you still feel you were wronged, let the other person know how you feel by calmly using I-Messages such as:
   • "I am annoyed that you acted that way."
   • "I feel angry when you say that."

Using I-Messages helps you take responsibility for your feelings rather than attacking or blaming the other person. Your goal is to let your feelings be heard—not to have an argument.

3. **Clarify.** Repeat back what you heard the other person say. This helps avoid assumptions or misunderstandings.

4. **Clean your side of the street.** This is another way of saying that you need to take responsibility for your part in the conflict.

5. **Be willing to compromise.** Work toward mutual solutions that satisfy both people.

6. **Clean it up.** Affirm, forgive, apologize, or thank the other person for being willing to work with you.

SUMMARY OF ACTIVITIES

This lesson taught you how to break the anger cycle, where anger leads to resentment, which leads to negative feelings, which leads to more anger and possibly relapse back to substance use. Keep practicing using the ABCD technique to manage and reduce anger.

■ ■ ■

Duplicating this page is illegal. Do not copy this material without written permission from the publisher.

69

LESSON 11

Introduction to Step Three

Thought for the Day	*"When [self-examination, meditation, and prayer] are . . . interwoven, the result is an unshakable foundation for life."* —*TWELVE STEPS AND TWELVE TRADITIONS*

REVIEW OF STEPS ONE AND TWO

In Step One we defined the problem:

- You have a body that can't handle alcohol and other drugs.

- You have a mind that can't give them up.

- In your active addiction, you had no spiritual connection to a Higher Power to help you.

Cycle of Addiction

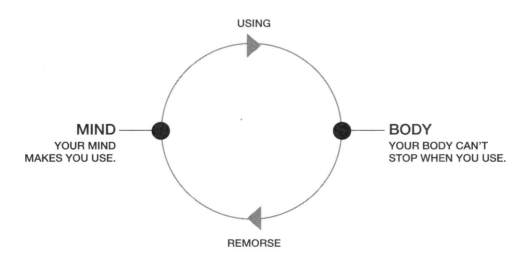

USING

MIND — YOUR MIND MAKES YOU USE.

BODY — YOUR BODY CAN'T STOP WHEN YOU USE.

REMORSE

Duplicating this page is illegal. Do not copy this material without written permission from the publisher.

71

In Step One we learned that we need help—we can't do it alone. In Step Two we learned that we start by believing that a Power greater than ourselves can restore us to sanity.

Step Three is about making a conscious decision to rely on this Higher Power for guidance.

Step Three is the last of the Preparation Steps that offer the solution to the problem of addiction. Steps Four to Nine ask us to take action so we can transform, and Steps Ten to Twelve help us continue to grow.

The Three Phases

Preparation	Transformation	Continued Transformation
Steps One through Three	**Steps Four through Nine**	**Steps Ten through Twelve**
The first three Steps prepare you for change. They focus on understanding your disease and knowing and seeking the solution.	Once you know the problem and the solution, you need to take action. By following these six Steps (also called "Action Steps" in AA), you will begin to see your life transformed.	Recovery is a lifelong journey. These three Steps (also called "Maintenance Steps" in AA) focus on actions you can take to continue your growth and maintain the success you have achieved day by day, for a lifetime.

Step Three: "Made a decision to turn our will and our lives over to the care of God *as we understood Him.*"

LETTING GO OF SELF-WILL

We started out thinking that our problem was alcohol and other drugs. But our problem is really our self-will. We want what we want when we want it. Read chapter 5 of the Big Book, "How It Works." Think about what the Big Book says about self-will being the root of our problems and what drives us to hurt others. This story describes each of us as "an actor who wants to run the whole show." We think that if things would run as we wish, then the show (i.e., life) would be great. When the show doesn't go well, we exert our control in more self-serving ways and eventually blame others for all our failures. The solution is to be rid of this "self-will run riot."

The Big Book explains how we can reduce this self-centeredness—by letting God, as you understand God (or your Higher Power), be the one who runs the show. We must choose to turn over our life and will to our Higher Power. Surrendering our will to our Higher Power is not a onetime decision. It is a daily practice.

Step Three Decision Tree

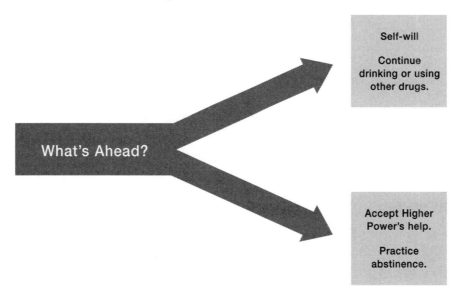

What's Ahead?

Self-will

Continue drinking or using other drugs.

Accept Higher Power's help.

Practice abstinence.

Duplicating this page is illegal. Do not copy this material without written permission from the publisher.

73

STEP THREE PRAYER

Making this decision to rely on our Higher Power for guidance in our lives is likely a bit different for everyone, but here is one example of a prayer from the Big Book that might help:

Step Three Prayer

"God, I offer myself to Thee—to build with me and to do with me as Thou wilt.

Relieve me of the bondage of self, that I may better do Thy will.

Take away my difficulties, that victory over them may bear witness to those I would help of Thy Power, Thy Love, and Thy Way of life.

May I do Thy will always!"

Take a minute to rewrite the Step Three prayer in your own words.

_____

_____

_____

_____

YOUR HIGHER POWER'S WILL

But how can you know what your Higher Power's will is for your life? Here are some simple tips:

- **Staying clean and sober is definitely your Higher Power's will for you.** Making decisions that protect your sobriety are aligned with your Higher Power's will.

- **"Do the next right thing."** We don't always know what our Higher Power's will is. But we usually know what the next right thing to do is. Continue to do the next right thing, and the will of your Higher Power will be revealed.

- **Talk with others in recovery.** Often our Higher Power uses others to guide us.

- **Pray and meditate.** These help you connect with your Higher Power, and over time, the will of your Higher Power will be revealed.

- **Cultivate an attitude of surrender.** As long as we hold on to our self-will run riot, we lose sight of our Higher Power's will. We must reduce our self-centeredness by letting our Higher Power run the show.

ACTIVITY

SURRENDERING OUR WILL

This activity will help you evaluate where you need help in surrendering.

Check the box next to the areas of your life where you are currently surrendering to your Higher Power.

I am surrendering . . .

- ☐ my addiction and my efforts to overcome my addiction
- ☐ my self-will and my desire to run my life my way
- ☐ my need to have life turn out the way I want it to
- ☐ my fears, worries, and anxieties
- ☐ my anger and resentments
- ☐ my need to do things perfectly and to make no mistakes
- ☐ my feelings of low self-worth, shame, and guilt
- ☐ my concerns about the future; my regrets about the past
- ☐ my need to be in control
- ☐ painful situations that have happened to me in the past
- ☐ my decisions and choices this day
- ☐ my relationship with my significant other
- ☐ my relationship with my children or other family members
- ☐ my other relationships
- ☐ my work situation (or lack of)
- ☐ other _____

continued

1. In what areas are you having trouble letting go?

   _____

   _____

   _____

   _____

   _____

2. What would help you let go of these things?

   _____

   _____

   _____

   _____

   _____

■

SELF-WILL VERSUS FREE WILL

Have you heard of free will? How is it different from self-will? Self-will is wanting what we want in self-serving ways. Self-will blocks us from having healthy relationships with our Higher Power, family, friends, coworkers, community, and others.

Free will is different. Free will is one of our greatest gifts. We can use our free will in the service of ourselves and others, to choose to do what is best for our recovery and for others around us. When we exert our free will, we are part of a larger picture.

Just for today, I will adjust myself to what is,
and not try to adjust everything else to my desires.
I will take my "luck" as it comes and fit myself into it.

Brent's Story

After I had been sober for a year, I gained an arrogant attitude about my recovery. I started to test my willpower by going with friends to bars or parties. I thought that I could drink just one beer and stop. I could tell that my self-will was running riot again. I talked to my sponsor, and he helped me focus on helping others instead of thinking about myself. I began to speak at meetings and stay late to talk with others. It kept me grounded and reminded me that I'm not the center of the universe. As I watched other people get better, they showed me how to improve my own recovery. When they stumbled, they showed me what mistakes to avoid.

ACTIVITY

PRACTICE POSITIVE FREE WILL

To exercise your free will and overcome self-will, do something positive. Make a commitment to help another person.

Check any of these positive things you are willing to do in the next week:

☐ Do an act of kindness for your significant other or a family member or friend.

☐ Drive a newcomer to the next Twelve Step meeting.

☐ Volunteer to set up chairs or make coffee for your next Twelve Step meeting.

☐ Write a note of appreciation to your sponsor or another person in recovery who has been there for you. Let him or her know you would like to return the favor.

☐ Share your story at your next Twelve Step meeting.

☐ Donate to the needy—money, food, clothes, time.

☐ Call your local Alcoholics Anonymous (AA) or Narcotics Anonymous (NA) Central Office and ask if they need volunteers.

Duplicating this page is illegal. Do not copy this material without written permission from the publisher.

77

THE PROMISES

Remember that the decision we make in Step Three is only as good as the actions we take in Steps Four through Nine. The harder you work to apply these next Steps, the more you will enjoy the promises that people talk about in Twelve Step programs.

For example, here are some promises we will experience as we continue to work Step Three:

- We find that our Higher Power provides what we need.
- More and more, we become interested in seeing what we can contribute to life.
- We discover that we can face life successfully.
- We become more conscious of our Higher Power's presence.
- We begin to lose our fear of today and tomorrow.

As you work the Steps, these promises will naturally become a part of your life. Make a commitment to talk to your sponsor or friends from an AA or NA meeting about your decision to seek guidance from a Higher Power. Ask others at meetings about making this decision in their lives.

Read the Twelve Steps article (in the Recovery Resources section at the end of this workbook) for more information about all Twelve Steps.

SUMMARY OF ACTIVITIES

This lesson taught the basic concept of Step Three—the importance of letting go of self-will and instead relying on a Higher Power for guidance. Make sure you read chapter 5 of the Big Book, "How It Works," about self-will as the root of our problems and Step Three as the solution.

■ ■ ■

Seek Guidance

| **Thought for the Day** | *"Grace is available for each of us every day—our spiritual daily bread—but we've got to remember to ask for it with a grateful heart and not worry about whether there will be enough for tomorrow."*
—SARAH BAN BREATHNACH |

PRACTICE SPIRITUALITY

The Twelve Steps teach us that we are not working a program of purely human effort; we are working a spiritual program. Having spirituality at the core of your recovery is key to your success. It is out of that spiritual core that all other progress in your life must flow.

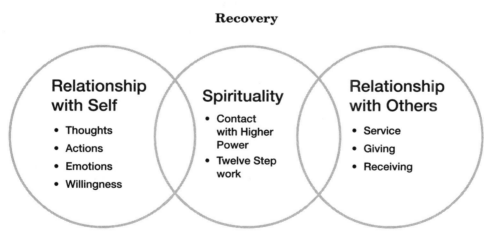

The Big Book tells us that "The answers will come, if your own house is in order." We keep our house in order by connecting with our Higher Power each day. It becomes easier to block out the cunning, baffling, and powerful voice of addiction when we feel spiritually connected with a Power greater than ourselves.

Duplicating this page is illegal. Do not copy this material without written permission from the publisher.

79

You can use prayer to talk with your Higher Power and meditation to listen to this Power.

Meditation and prayer are tools. They can help you let go of self-will, bring a sense of calm and well-being, and deepen your relationship with your Higher Power.

Read chapter 6 of the Big Book, "Into Action," for guidance on starting your day with help from your Higher Power.

Prayer and Meditation

Practice prayer and meditation daily so you are ready for any unexpected thoughts and overwhelming feelings. Ask friends in recovery how they use prayer and meditation in their lives.

Prayer is talking to our Higher Power.

- Pray for courage to change or confront the situations that frighten you.
- Pray for others—even those you don't like or have anger toward.
- Pray for resolution to your anger.
- Pray to relieve fear, grief, and anger that can lead you toward a return to substance use.
- Pray to bring a sense of calm and well-being—a sense that you are part of a greater whole.

Meditation is listening to our Higher Power.

- Meditate to clear your mind of stressful thoughts.
- Meditate to restore a sense of calmness.
- Use a guided meditation audio. (You can find meditation apps or meditation audio online.)

Trust in Your Higher Power

As you learn more about the Twelve Steps, you're learning that no human power can relieve your addiction. The solution is to turn to a Power greater than yourself for help. This is what the spiritual journey in recovery is all about. Lasting recovery comes from trusting your Higher Power and staying connected with your Higher Power through prayer and meditation each day.

Learn from Others

Listening to others' stories at Twelve Step meetings is another way to build trust in your Higher Power. In their stories, you may learn that their lives, like yours, were disrupted or maybe nearly destroyed by their addictions—and yet, in their recovery, they found a solution.

Practice Gratitude

Another way to build trust and confidence in your Higher Power is to take time each day to focus on the positive and develop an attitude of gratitude. Some days you may be grateful only for the fact that you are sober. On other days, you may have a whole list of things you are thankful for. Cultivate an attitude of gratitude by completing the next activity, which asks you to identify the ways your Higher Power is helping in your life.

ACTIVITY

ATTITUDE OF GRATITUDE

Cultivate an attitude of gratitude by making a list of the things you are grateful for and the things your Higher Power is helping you with.

I am grateful for:

_____

_____

_____

_____

_____

_____

My Higher Power is helping me with:

_____

_____

_____

_____

_____

SUMMARY OF ACTIVITIES

This lesson taught you the importance of connecting with a Higher Power and the role of prayer and meditation in recovery. Make sure you read the Big Book chapter "Into Action." Use the activity Attitude of Gratitude to stay connected to the things you are grateful for.

■ ■ ■

Surrender Your Fears

| **Thought for the Day** | *"Fear is nothing more or less than a distorted faith in the negative things of life and the evils that might beset us."*
 —THE LITTLE RED BOOK |

DEALING WITH FEAR AND WORRY IN EARLY RECOVERY

Many people in early recovery are afraid of returning to substance use, and of facing friends and family they have hurt. We also worry about being around the people we used to drink or use drugs with. This is normal. We do need to avoid people who could cause us to relapse. We also need to find positive ways to handle fear and worry instead of turning to substances.

Look at the list below and identify which fears and worries you are struggling with right now.

☐ returning to alcohol or other drug use

☐ facing friends and family I've hurt

☐ being around risky people or risky situations

☐ returning to work and/or coping with daily responsibilities

☐ fears about past emotions or events

☐ other _____

A lot of energy we put toward worry and fear is wasted:

• Many of our fears never happen.

• Many of our fears are about things in the past that cannot be changed.

• Some of our fears are based on inaccurate beliefs about how we think others see us.

• Some of our fears are about health matters, but stressing only makes these worse.

What all this means is that many of our fears cause us to worry unnecessarily. The good news is that fear can be managed. With the help of a Higher Power and our friends in recovery, we can **F**ace **E**verything **A**nd **R**ecover.

TYPES OF FEARS

There are four types of fears that are common in early recovery. These include:

1. **Fear of facing the past.** In recovery, we must eventually face our past and the harms we caused when we were using. We also need to face harms that others have done to us. Using your support system while you face the past will make it less scary and less stressful. You are not alone. You have your Twelve Step friends and your Higher Power guiding you through this process.

Living in fear is like paying interest on a loan you don't owe.

2. **Fear of relapse triggers.** Certain people and places threaten your sobriety, so it is important to stay away from them. Many of us fear that we won't manage risky situations well or that we will make our same old mistakes. When you worry, reach out to your counselor, sponsor, or Twelve Step friends. They've been there and understand. You will find that managing your relapse triggers gets easier over time. As we form new healthy habits, we no longer struggle as much each day. Rather than drinking or drugs being the focus of our habits, we start to automatically engage in positive things like going to meetings, exercising, and spending time with supportive people.

3. **Fear of facing relationships.** You may also worry about how your relationships with others may change now that you are in recovery. You may have lost some friends since you started recovery. But what new friends have you made? How about the relationship with your sponsor? You can reduce your worry by focusing on the positive growth in your life and keep working recovery one day at a time.

4. **Fear of living sober.** Does the idea of living the rest of your life without substances scare you? This is why it is so important to commit to staying sober one day at a time. You don't have to do this alone. Turn your fears over to your Higher Power. As the expression goes, "Let go and let God."

COPE WITH FEAR AND WORRY

Use the following strategies to face and manage your fears:

- **Acceptance.** Fear is normal. Accept it and choose to be uncomfortable for today rather than returning to alcohol and other drug use.
- **Easy does it.** Worrying about things that we can't control or change is a waste of energy. Live each day one day at a time.
- **Put it on a shelf.** We can't resolve everything at once. Put your worries on a shelf and resolve them one at a time with the support of others.
- **Let go and let God.** Turn your life and will (and worries) over to your Higher Power. Connect with your Higher Power by practicing prayer and meditation.
- **Stay motivated.** Commit to work your recovery program at least for today.
- **Be involved.** The more you engage in sober activities, the less time you have to worry.
- **Seek help.** If you are not in a safe environment, seek help right away.

ACTIVITY

WORRY JURY

Are worries causing you trouble? It's time to put them on trial. This activity will help you challenge your worries and decide whether they are worth it. This will help you gain a sense of control over what is bothering you.

As you answer the questions below, you will "cross-examine" your biggest worries. Consider the evidence and decide for yourself whether your worries are worth it.

1. What is one of your biggest worries?

_____

_____

continued

2. What are your fears about this worry? What bad things do you think might happen?

_____

_____

3. What are you telling yourself about this situation that makes you more upset about it?

_____

_____

4. If this worry did come true, what is the worst thing that could happen?

_____

_____

5. What is your anxiety level about this worry? (0–100 scale) _____

6. How strong is the evidence that the worst thing will actually happen? (0–100 scale) _____

7. If the worst thing happens, is it possible that you could learn to deal with it?

☐ Yes   ☐ No

8. How could you cope?

_____

_____

"I am an old man and have known a great many troubles, but most of them have never happened."

—Mark Twain

9. What is a more likely and possibly better outcome?

_____

_____

10. What level is your anxiety now about this worry? (0–100 scale) _____

Keep in mind: worry can be a good thing, as long as we actively seek solutions to our problems. There are things you can do that can help you take the panic out of worry and teach you how to use it to your advantage. Continue to put your worries on trial to help gain a sense of control.

■

SUMMARY OF ACTIVITIES

This lesson taught you how to deal with fear and worry in early recovery. This includes facing fear of past events, relapse triggers, living sober, and facing relationships with others. It includes the Worry Jury activity, which asks us to face worries and decide if they are worth it. Whenever you find yourself stressed, complete the Worry Jury activity.

■ ■ ■

Stay Grounded

Thought for the Day	*"Learn daily the lesson of trust and calm in the midst of the storms of life. Whatever of sorrow or difficulty the day may bring, God's command to you is the same. Be grateful, humble, calm, and loving to all people. Leave each soul the better for having met you or heard you. For all kinds of people, this should be your attitude: a loving desire to help and an infectious spirit of calmness and trust in God. You have the answer to loneliness and fear, which is calm faith in the goodness and purpose in the universe."*
	—*TWENTY-FOUR HOURS A DAY, JULY 1*

MAKING PROGRESS

There is no end to the journey of recovery, so how do you know if you are making progress? Is recovery just about staying abstinent? Or is there more to it?

Check any of these signs of growth and success in recovery that you have noticed.

- ☐ being more at peace with myself

- ☐ having fewer cravings and urges to use

- ☐ feeling the desire to give back to others

- ☐ noticing that relationships with friends and family are healthier

- ☐ participating in "normal" society as I define "normal"

- ☐ being a more positive person

Ask your sponsor, counselor, or recovery friends for help in the areas where you are struggling.

FOCUS ON SPIRITUALITY

The Steps teach us that we are not working a program of purely human effort; we are working a spiritual program. Having spirituality at the core of your recovery is essential to your success. It is out of that spiritual core that all other progress in your life must flow.

Jamie's Story

During my first few months of recovery, I thought it was all about staying abstinent by giving up all drug use, but I found out that it's really so much more than that. Abstinence is only the beginning. Over time, I realized that my recovery was more about my spiritual growth and becoming a healthier person. I am becoming so much more confident, content, and peaceful. I am becoming the person I was always meant to be.

WATCH OUT FOR HALT

We must continue to watch out for HALT symptoms. Becoming too hungry, angry, lonely, or tired can lead to relapse.

Hungry

Regular mealtimes and nutritious meals are essential to our long-term recovery and to regaining our physical and mental health.

Angry

Unresolved anger can turn into resentment, and resentment can lead to a relapse. Use the Relapse Prevention Strategies handout (found in the Recovery Resources section at the end of this workbook) to keep stress from turning into anger and resentment.

Lonely

Keep loneliness at bay by seeking connections and turning to the Twelve Step fellowship and recovery community for help whenever you need it. No matter how long you have been in recovery, you still can't recover on your own. Stay clean and sober one day at a time by staying connected with the recovery community.

Tired

Make sure you schedule regular times for going to bed and waking up. Being alert and rested allows you to better make healthy lifestyle changes.

MANAGE URGES AND CRAVINGS

Over time in recovery, we start to feel more confident, but we may still experience urges or cravings that take us by surprise. This is normal. Even after a year of sobriety, urges and cravings can crop up when you least expect them.

If you are still experiencing cravings, which people, places, or things cause them?

_____

_____

_____

_____

_____

_____

Tips for handling a craving:

1. **Remove yourself from the high-risk situation and get to a safe place.** Go to an Alcoholics Anonymous (AA) or other Twelve Step meeting right away, if possible.

2. **Contact your sponsor and talk about how you are feeling.** Remember, thoughts about using are normal—they are not a sign of weakness. Calling someone to talk about what you're experiencing at the moment can help to relax, soften, or even end the urge. Other people in recovery have been there, too, and they understand the need to talk about these intense feelings.

"Those who slip know they can reclaim the program if they choose. Nothing is entirely lost and their Higher Power is always there, ready to help."

—Adapted from *Twenty-Four Hours a Day*

AVOID OVERCONFIDENCE

As we spend more time in recovery, it's easy to start thinking that we have overcome our addiction and don't have to worry about it anymore. Don't make this mistake. The truth is that you are only one drink or hit away from danger. The spiritual focus that has helped you achieve sobriety is the same focus you need to maintain it. This reminds you that you are powerless. You are not God—you are a person with an addiction. This helps you stay out of the driver's seat.

We avoid relapse by staying watchful for relapse warning signs. We know that relapse can start long before the drink or hit is taken. Relapse starts with the thoughts and emotions that set you up to want to take a drink or hit. If you don't apply relapse prevention strategies when these thoughts and emotions occur, they could lead to a return to use.

The key to avoiding relapse is to stay vigilant and aware, and continue to do the things that support your recovery, such as going to meetings, working with a sponsor, and connecting with a Higher Power.

ACTIVITY

KEEPING RECOVERY A PRIORITY

The things below are important ways to keep your recovery a top priority. Check all of these that you are doing consistently.

☐ Attend AA or Narcotics Anonymous (NA) meetings.

☐ Read Twelve Step literature, such as the Big Book, or daily meditation books about recovery, such as the book *Twenty-Four Hours a Day*.

☐ Talk with your sponsor and Twelve Step friends regularly.

☐ Cut back or eliminate an activity if it distracts you from focusing on your sobriety.

☐ Avoid stress. Evaluate your schedule and say no to a few things that don't have to be a priority right now.

☐ Use prayer and meditation to connect with your Higher Power and build your serenity. Try using a guided meditation audio. (You can find meditation apps or meditation audio online.)

☐ Update your daily schedule, Recovery Wallet Card, and Relapse Prevention Plan so that you know how to avoid and cope with risky situations. (These are found in the Recovery Resources section at the end of this workbook.)

DEAL WITH RELAPSE

Regardless of our best intentions, some people relapse back to use of alcohol or other drugs. If you relapse, do the following:

- Ask for help to stop using.
- Get out of the situation.
- Repeat the following:
    - "I made a mistake."
    - "I feel guilty, but that's normal."
    - "I will stay calm."
    - "One slip does not equal failure."
    - "I can learn from this experience."
    - "I can recommit to my recovery."

These tips for dealing with relapse are listed on the Recovery Wallet Card (found in the Recovery Resources section at the end of this workbook). Keep a copy of the Recovery Wallet Card with you at all times for tips for stopping a relapse.

If you relapse, focusing on the negative leads to guilt, blame, and resentment toward yourself. Focusing on the negative will sabotage the positive progress you've made in recovery. Instead, look at relapse as a temporary setback. If you've been using for a while, you may need professional help for withdrawal. An unsupervised detoxification could be dangerous. Consult a reputable addiction treatment center for help. Never try to handle a relapse alone.

SUMMARY OF ACTIVITIES

This lesson taught you how to stay grounded over time in recovery by watching out for HALT (hungry, angry, lonely, tired), managing cravings, avoiding overconfidence, practicing relapse prevention, and appreciating our spiritual growth. Make sure you keep your Recovery Wallet Card, daily schedule, and Relapse Prevention Plan with you for easy reference.

■ ■ ■

Duplicating this page is illegal. Do not copy this material without written permission from the publisher.

93

Recovery Resources

Workbook 3

Daily Schedule

Photocopy this form, so you have one for each day of the week. Then fill in each hour of the schedule.

Daily Schedule

Day of the Week (circle one):   M   T   W   Th   F   Sat   Sun

A.M.	6:00:	_____
	7:00:	_____
	8:00:	_____
	9:00:	_____
	10:00:	_____
	11:00:	_____
P.M.	Noon:	_____
	1:00:	_____
	2:00:	_____
	3:00:	_____
	4:00:	_____
	5:00:	_____
	6:00:	_____
	7:00:	_____
	8:00:	_____
	9:00:	_____
	10:00:	_____
	11:00:	_____

Notes:

Reminders

Ask yourself these questions:

- Have I filled in gaps of time?
- Have I scheduled time to connect with my sponsor and Higher Power?
- Have I identified and planned for high-risk situations?
- Did I make my recovery activities a priority?
- Is my day too busy or too stressful?
- Did I schedule time to attend at least one Twelve Step meeting per week?
- Have I shared my plan with others?

Keep this schedule with you at all times.
If you use a smartphone or computer calendar, input the schedule into that system so you see it every day.

Recovery Wallet Card

Step 1: Write down the names and contact information for three people you know you can count on to support your recovery.

Step 2: Write down three reasons why you want to stay sober. Make sure your reasons are about gaining something positive for yourself and not about avoiding something negative.

Step 3: Write down the names, addresses, and meeting times for nearby Twelve Step meetings you can attend. You can include other recovery resources, such as the addresses and times for addiction treatment meetings or meetings with a mental health counselor or other provider.

Step 4: Keep a copy of the Recovery Wallet Card with you at all times. It's also a good idea to input your supporters into your phone contacts.

Recovery Wallet Card Example

My supporters:	**My reasons for being in recovery:**
Name: Wesley A. **Phone:** 612-495-XXXX **Name:** Jennifer A. **Phone:** 651-375-XXXX **Name:** Mike R. (my sponsor) **Phone:** 651-984-XXXX	1. Become someone whom I and others respect. 2. Heal with my mom/love my mom. 3. Be good to myself and others. Happy life. *"One day at a time"*
My recovery resources/meetings:	**END YOUR LAPSE**

Name: Sober Friends (Cafe Coffee Shop)
 Address: 9459 W. 28th St., Minneapolis, MN 55408
 Day/Time: M–F, 7 a.m.
 	
 Name: Big Book Study Group
 Address: 4241 Lyndale Ave., Minneapolis, MN 55408
 Day/Time: Wed., 6 p.m.
 	
 Name: Solution Seekers (Santi Community Center)
 Address: 1945 Hawkens St. NW, Eagan, MN 55122
 Day/Time: Sat., 6 p.m.
	1. ASK FOR HELP TO STOP USING
	 2. GET OUT OF THE SITUATION
	 3. REPEAT THE FOLLOWING
	   • *I made a mistake.*
	   • *I feel guilty, but that's normal.*
	   • *I will stay calm.*
	   • *One slip does not equal failure.*
	   • *I can learn from this experience.*
	   • *I can recommit to my recovery.*

Your Recovery Wallet Card

Fill out your information.

cut on solid line

My supporters:

Name: _____

Phone: _____

Name: _____

Phone: _____

Name: _____

Phone: _____

My reasons for being in recovery:

1. _____

2. _____

3. _____

"One day at a time"

← fold in half
on dotted line

My recovery resources/meetings:

Name: _____

Address: _____

Day/Time: _____

Name: _____

Address: _____

Day/Time: _____

Name: _____

Address: _____

Day/Time: _____

END YOUR LAPSE

1. ASK FOR HELP TO STOP USING
2. GET OUT OF THE SITUATION
3. REPEAT THE FOLLOWING
   - *I made a mistake.*
   - *I feel guilty, but that's normal.*
   - *I will stay calm.*
   - *One slip does not equal failure.*
   - *I can learn from this experience.*
   - *I can recommit to my recovery.*

← fold in half
on dotted line

Twelve Steps

Where Did the Twelve Steps Come From?

Until 1934, there was no known addiction treatment that worked. Later that year, Bill W. and Dr. Bob started a group called Alcoholics Anonymous (AA) and eventually wrote the Twelve Steps to offer simple, straightforward principles, or basic truths, that people can follow to recover from addiction. The Twelve Steps express the fundamental principles used by members of AA to transform their lives from moral decay and early death to a spiritual fitness needed to keep the disease of addiction at bay.

THE TWELVE STEPS OF ALCOHOLICS ANONYMOUS

1. We admitted we were powerless over alcohol [or other drugs]—that our lives had become unmanageable.

2. Came to believe that a Power greater than ourselves could restore us to sanity.

3. Made a decision to turn our will and our lives over to the care of God *as we understood Him.*

4. Made a searching and fearless moral inventory of ourselves.

5. Admitted to God, to ourselves, and to another human being the exact nature of our wrongs.

6. Were entirely ready to have God remove all these defects of character.

7. Humbly asked Him to remove our shortcomings.

8. Made a list of all persons we had harmed, and became willing to make amends to them all.

9. Made direct amends to such people wherever possible, except when to do so would injure them or others.

10. Continued to take personal inventory and when we were wrong promptly admitted it.

11. Sought through prayer and meditation to improve our conscious contact with God *as we understood Him,* praying only for knowledge of His will for us and the power to carry that out.

12. Having had a spiritual awakening as the result of these steps, we tried to carry this message to alcoholics, and to practice these principles in all our affairs.*

* Reprinted from *Alcoholics Anonymous,* 4th ed. (New York: Alcoholics Anonymous World Services, Inc., 2001), 59–60.

Relapse Prevention Plan

PART 1

This activity will help you create your own personalized relapse prevention plan. This is a three-part activity. Be sure to complete all three parts. Also, periodically update your relapse prevention plan as your routines and environment change.

It is important to identify your high-risk situations or events when you used to drink or use other drugs. These situations or events can be stressful and pose a direct threat to your recovery. It pays to be prepared and plan out the coping strategies you will use.

1. Name four PEOPLE (by first name only to preserve confidentiality) you used with before treatment who are still using and whom you might or will meet again.

   1. _____
   2. _____
   3. _____
   4. _____

2. Write down the names of four PLACES where you used in the past that might still be tempting for you.

   1. _____
   2. _____
   3. _____
   4. _____

3. Name four THINGS that you used to get high (e.g., needles, pipes, money, razors, mirrors, or pills) that might trigger a craving.

   1. _____
   2. _____
   3. _____
   4. _____

4. Describe four HABITS that you had and might still associate with using
    (e.g., taking a certain route to work, driving by a dealer's house, going to a
    liquor store, or seeing commercials, logos, or clothing).

    1. _____

    2. _____

    3. _____

    4. _____

5. List four EMOTIONS that could cause a craving (e.g., angry, sad, scared,
    excited, or bored).

    1. _____

    2. _____

    3. _____

    4. _____

6. List four CONDITIONS that might start a craving (e.g., being out of touch
    with support people, HALT [hungry, angry, lonely, tired], medical problems, or
    poverty).

    1. _____

    2. _____

    3. _____

    4. _____

7. Review the high-risk situations/triggers that you listed above. Write down
    the four most important HIGH-RISK SITUATIONS from these lists.

    1. _____

    2. _____

    3. _____

    4. _____

Relapse Prevention Plan

PART 2

Now that you have made the decision to quit drinking and using drugs, you will begin to feel more confident about staying sober, and this confidence will grow as you continue your recovery journey. However, you still need to plan for risky situations that pose a threat to your recovery. This relapse prevention plan will help you watch for relapse warning signs.

1. List three negative emotional states (e.g., anger, anxiety, depression, frustration, boredom, or grief).

   1. _____
   2. _____
   3. _____

2. What do you intend to do when you find yourself feeling these emotional states?

   1. _____
   2. _____
   3. _____

3. Situations that cause you to experience challenging emotional states and conflict in relationships will put you at a high risk of relapse. List three possible situations and people who might produce challenging emotions or conflict in your life.

   Situations

   1. _____
   2. _____
   3. _____

   People

   1. _____
   2. _____
   3. _____

4. What do you intend to do when you find yourself in these negative emotional states?

    1. _____

    2. _____

    3. _____

5. Describe three examples of social pressure (including verbal or nonverbal persuasion or indirect pressure) that might lead you to return to substance use.

    1. _____

    2. _____

    3. _____

6. What do you intend to do when you find yourself in situations where you feel social pressure?

    1. _____

    2. _____

    3. _____

7. List three positive emotional states that you think could be a problem for you (e.g., happiness, excitement, feeling comfortable, or wanting to celebrate).

    1. _____

    2. _____

    3. _____

8. What do you intend to do when you find yourself feeling these positive emotional states?

    1. _____

    2. _____

    3. _____

9. Give three examples of times when you rationalized your use (e.g., buying a bottle of liquor in case a guest drops in). Denial and a desire for immediate gratification will increase your vulnerability to return to substance use.

   1. _____

   2. _____

   3. _____

10. What do you intend to do when you find yourself rationalizing or denying these situations?

    1. _____

    2. _____

    3. _____

11. A balanced lifestyle has been found to be the strongest defense against relapse. What areas of your life are out of balance?

    1. _____

    2. _____

    3. _____

12. What do you intend to do when you find your life out of balance?

    1. _____

    2. _____

    3. _____

13. What have you been doing (or not doing) for your physical well-being lately?

    _____

    _____

    _____

    _____

    _____

14. What have you been doing (or not doing) for your mental well-being lately?

_____

_____

_____

_____

_____

15. What have you been doing (or not doing) for your spiritual well-being lately?

_____

_____

_____

_____

_____

Keep in Mind: Structure and overall balance are critical for staying in recovery. And remember, if you need support, you can call one of your contacts from your Recovery Wallet Card, including your sponsor, counselor, supportive family members, or friends from meetings.

Relapse Prevention Plan

PART 3

Finding Support: It is important to know where you can find help when you need it.

1. List five people (by first name only) you can call for help when you need it.

    1. _____
    2. _____
    3. _____
    4. _____
    5. _____

2. List five places (addresses and phone numbers) where you can go for help when you need it.

    1. _____
    2. _____
    3. _____
    4. _____
    5. _____

3. List five thoughts that will motivate you to prevent a relapse.

    1. _____
    2. _____
    3. _____
    4. _____
    5. _____

4. If you are unable to follow the strategies in this relapse prevention plan, what can you do?

_____

_____

_____

_____

_____

Remember that your counselor and sponsor are there for you. All you need to do is reach out.

Relapse Prevention Strategies

1. Are there certain times of day that are very stressful for you? Are there days or times (such as payday or the weekend) when you previously used drugs?

   Strategies:
   - Plan to call your sponsor or a friend in recovery at this time.
   - Plan a fun sober activity to do during this time.
   - If possible, attend a Twelve Step meeting during this period of time.
   - Plan to be with other people who are supportive of your recovery during this time.
   - Plan to work on your program during this time—read the Big Book, Twelve Step literature, or a meditation book; spend time in meditation.

2. Are there stretches of time when you will be alone?

   Strategies:
   - Try to limit the long periods of time that you are spending alone.
   - Plan to call your sponsor or a friend in recovery at this time.
   - Plan a fun sober activity to do during this time.
   - If possible, attend a Twelve Step meeting during this time.
   - Plan to be with other people who are supportive of your recovery during this time.

3. Are there events that will be stressful for you?

   Strategies:
   - If possible, avoid this stressful situation.
   - Limit the number of stressful situations you have in your day. Can you say no to something?
   - Before you go to this stressful event, call your sponsor or a friend in recovery. Talk through strategies to handle the stress.
   - Have a plan of "escape" if the situation becomes too stressful—drive separately to the event, for example.
   - Make a plan to call your sponsor or a friend in recovery right after the stressful event.
   - Go to a Twelve Step meeting right after the stressful event.

- Plan an enjoyable sober activity to do right after the stressful event.
- Spend some time in meditation before and after the event.
- Use breathing exercises to calm yourself during the event.

4. Are there any high-risk situations for you this week (people and places you should avoid)? Avoid these high-risk situations—the places where you used to use and places where other people will be using.

Tips for avoiding places:

- Take a different route so you avoid certain places.
- Ask people to meet you at locations that will not trigger use for you— for example, meet at a coffee shop rather than a bar.
- Ask other people to drive, so you aren't tempted to go places you shouldn't.
- Turn down invitations to events where alcohol or other drugs might be present.

Tips for avoiding people:

- Politely say no to people you need to avoid.
- Honestly tell people that you are in recovery now and need to protect your sobriety.
- Get rid of the phone numbers and email addresses of people you used to use with.
- Don't go to places where you know these people will be.
- Avoid all contact, even by phone, with these people.

If you can't avoid a situation, use these coping strategies:

- Ask someone who is supportive of your recovery to go with you.
- Talk through the situation with your sponsor or a friend in recovery before going.
- Write out a plan of how you are going to handle the situation. Create this plan with the help of a friend in recovery. Carry this plan with you.
- Commit to call your sponsor or a friend in recovery right after the event or situation.
- Have an "escape" plan to get out of the situation if it becomes too difficult for you.
- Plan to go to a Twelve Step event right afterward.

About Hazelden Publishing

As part of the Hazelden Betty Ford Foundation, Hazelden Publishing offers both cutting-edge educational resources and inspirational books. Our print and digital works help guide individuals in treatment and recovery, and their loved ones. Professionals who work to prevent and treat addiction also turn to Hazelden Publishing for evidence-based curricula, digital content solutions, and videos for use in schools, treatment programs, correctional programs, and electronic health records systems. We also offer training for implementation of our curricula.

Through published and digital works, Hazelden Publishing extends the reach of healing and hope to individuals, families, and communities affected by addiction and related issues.

For more information about Hazelden publications,
please call **800-328-9000**
or visit us online at **hazelden.org/bookstore**.